CHECKLIST OF PROTECTED BRITISH SPECIES

FAUNA & FLORA PROTECTED BY BRITISH AND INTERNATIONAL LEGAL INSTRUMENTS
ARRANGED ALPHABETICALLY BY SCIENTIFIC AND COMMON ENGLISH NAMES

Compiled by Christopher J. Betts

with illustrations by Leone A. Betts

Second Edition
(updated following the coming into force of the Countryside
and Rights of Way Act)

Published by

CHRISTOPHER BETTS ENVIRONMENTAL BIOLOGY
Monkwood Green
Worcester, U.K.

VERSION 02.2/CBEB 0501

© Christopher Betts Environmental Biology
ISBN 1 9000 2303 2

First edition published 1996 (1 9000 2301 6)
Second (revised and updated) edition 1998
Reprinted with minor corrections and amendments 2000
Reprinted 2001 (pursuant to the Countryside and Rights of Way Act)

Printed in Great Britain by B. J. Lander & Sons Ltd., Worcester.

CONTENTS

IMPORTANT NOTES

All the species currently listed in the major schedules and appendices of the main statutory instruments protecting fauna and flora in Britain (England, Scotland, Wales and offshore islands)[a] are included in this Checklist. The acts, schedules and appendices included are described in the Key to Abbreviations below which gives a brief summary of the protection afforded. However, readers must refer to the published acts and conventions for full details and should be aware both that legislation can change rapidly and that there may be other instruments in force beyond the intended scope of this publication. For example, there are complex rules affecting fisheries.

The greatest changes in this update of the Checklist relate to the new Countryside and Rights of Way Act, at least inasmuch as England and Wales are concerned where this is the most significant wildlife legislation since 1981. The Act scarcely affect the lists of protected species, but it does reflect a fundamental shift in wildlife protection philosophy and enforcement. It is far-reaching and complex - its text required fifty-one pages of explanatory notes, not a very good advertisement for clarity of writing.

The Checklist's species are arranged in alphabetical lists of invertebrate animals, fish, amphibians and reptiles, birds, mammals, non-vascular plants and vascular plants. The first set of lists is ordered by scientific name and the second set by vernacular (English) name. Although I have attempted to apply the English names which are most popularly used, readers should be aware that there are many Always, therefore, check the Tables of scientific names to be sure.

Please note that scientific nomenclature follows that used by the legal instruments which may ignore some very recent taxonomic changes. An Appendix (Table 8) is also given of those continental European protected species which are not British natives but which have become established in Britain through escapes or deliberate introductions.

Whilst the list of taxa given is, to my belief and from my researches of current publications, as accurate as possible at the time of writing (May 2001), this is an evolving subject, more so than ever with government devolution gathering pace. Species which have been afforded protection are usually, although not always, the very ones which tend to be most vulnerable: like all populations, they are subject to changes in their environment and related ecological factors - predation, competition, habitat loss, isolation, disease, pollution, climatic extremes, genetic effects operating on small populations and disturbance of all kinds may affect their status. In a relatively small and varied area like Great Britain, which is overwhelmingly influenced by the activities of man, changes in status can be rapid and pronounced. Reviews of status are carried out periodically by the regulatory bodies and schedules are updated accordingly. Biodiversity Action Plans have effectively been given legal backing by the Countryside and Rights of Way Act: government departments have a duty to have regard to conserving biological diversity and must publish lists of species of principle importance

As previously, it is planned to continue issuing further editions of this Checklist from time to time. Please remember that the information is given in good faith but does not purport in any way to give any advice on or interpretation of the law whatsoever. Professional legal advice should always be sought.

Readers can obtain specialist advice through the local offices of English Nature, Scottish National Heritage or the Countryside Council for Wales, from legal firms specializing in environmental law or from most environmental consultancies. Maximum penalties for contravention of the wildlife legislation in Britain are high (fines and even imprisonment) and, in England and Wales, have been greatly increased by the new law, so it is wise to obtain sound expert advice.

---

[a] None of Ireland is covered by the checklist. Differences in legislation and regulations between England, Scotland, Wales, the Isle of Man, *etc.* continue to accrue. Readers are advised to research the detail carefully through their professional advisers. The Countryside and Rights of Way Act does not apply to Scotland although there are proposals in the wings which, if adopted, will be similar.

KEY TO ABBREVIATIONS

Code	Full Title	Explanation
BC1	Appendix I of Berne Convention (Convention on the Conservation of European Wildlife and Natural Habitats)	The Berne Convention is designed to protect important populations of listed species and their habitats. This Appendix lists flora which are required to be specially protected against deliberate picking, collecting, cutting, uprooting, possession, sale, *etc.* See also below.
BC2	Appendix II of Berne Convention (Convention on the Conservation of European Wildlife and Natural Habitats)	This Appendix lists strictly protected fauna. The Berne Convention places particular emphasis on migratory species and their breeding and resting sites (see also Bonn below). Listed fauna are required to be strictly protected against deliberate killing, capture, damage/destruction of breeding and nesting sites, disturbance, taking of eggs, trading (including parts or derivatives), *etc.* Various exceptions can be invoked to avoid, for example, inappropriate situations arising over species which, although listed, are common and widespread.
BC3	Appendix III of Berne Convention (Convention on the Conservation of European Wildlife and Natural Habitats)	Listed in this Appendix are all animals not on Appendix II whose populations are required to be protected from exploitation (indiscriminate mass killing, trading and any means capable of causing local disappearance or serious disturbance to a species) and managed to keep them out of danger. The Appendix includes nearly all other birds (see note to Table 4A), all other reptiles and amphibians and many other mammals.
BoC1	Appendix I of Bonn Convention on the Conservation of Migratory Species of Wild Animals	Species on Appendix I are considered to be in danger of extinction and require stringent efforts to ensure strict protection from virtually any threat. "Migratory" is a broad term and includes dispersal, recruitment, etc.
BoC2	Appendix II of Bonn Convention on the Conservation of Migratory Species of Wild Animals	Appendix II species are generally of conservation concern and/or deemed to be able to benefit from international co-operation. Signatories are encouraged to draw up agreements (several have been or are being concluded) to restore/maintain species' conservation status through management and other appropriate measures. Please see note on birds at beginning of Tables 4A/4B
CITES1	Appendix I of Convention on International Trade in Endangered Species of Wild Fauna and Flora[a]	CITES, as its name suggests, is aimed at controlling international trade in wild plants and animals or "any recognisable part or derivative" of them (but there are exclusions in some cases for seeds, pollen, seedlings/tissue obtained *in vitro*, and cut flowers of artificially propagated plants). Appendix I taxa are considered to be in danger of extinction and trade in them is generally prohibited.
CITES2	Appendix II of Convention on International Trade in Endangered Species of Wild Fauna and Flora	The taxa on CITES Appendix II are listed because they are considered to be vulnerable to serious threat or extinction if trade is not controlled.
CITES3	Appendix III of Convention on International Trade in Endangered Species of Wild Fauna and Flora	These are taxa which a signatory country regards as vulnerable to exploitation and needing the co-operation of other signatories to control trade. *NB.* Species which **only** appear on this Appendix are not included in the Checklist.

---

[a]   CITES is enforced in Britain by the Control of Trade in Endangered Species (Enforcement) Regulations 1997.

Code	Full Title	Explanation
CSA	Conservation of Seals Act 1970	This Act prohibits certain methods of killing all seals, sets close seasons for certain taxa and allows the issuing of conservation orders including that of 19 December 1999 which prohibits the killing, injuring or taking of grey and common seals in English waters.
DA	Deer Act 1991	This Act consolidates previous legislation. Poaching, taking or killing at night or in the close season are prohibited (with certain exceptions). The sale of venison and the use of certain types of firearm are also controlled.
DSA	Deer (Scotland) Act 1996	A relatively extensive Act which enforces a wide range of controls through the Deer Commission for Scotland in that country (close seasons; unlawful killing, taking, injuring, driving, selling and possessing deer; poaching; licensing of venison dealing; game licences, crop damage *etc.*)
ECB	European Communities Council Directive on the Conservation of Wild Birds	This Directive relates to the conservation of all species of birds naturally occurring in the wild in the European territory of the Member States (but not Greenland), as well as their nests and habitats. A list of taxa (species and subspecies) requiring special conservation measures, such as designation and maintenance of Special Protection Areas, is cited in Annex I to this Directive and it is these species which are included in this Checklist. Birds generally are protected from deliberate killing, taking from the wild, egg collecting, nest destruction and keeping in captivity, but allowances are made for game birds. Pest species can be derogated by Member States (carrion crow, collared dove, feral and wood pigeons, rook, jackdaw, great and lesser black-backed gulls, herring gull, jay, magpie, house sparrow and starling in Britain).
ECH2	Annex II of the European Communities Council Directive on the Conservation of Natural Habitats and Wild Fauna and Flora[a]	Animal and plant species of community interest whose conservation requires the designation of Special Areas of Conservation (SACs).
ECH4	Annex IV of the European Communities Council Directive on the Conservation of Natural Habitats and Wild Fauna and Flora	Animal and plant species of community interest in need of strict protection. Damage or destruction of breeding sites or resting places are prohibited, and all life stages are protected against (as appropriate) deliberate capture, killing, disturbance, destruction of eggs, picking, collecting, cutting, uprooting or destruction in the wild as well as (except for specimens taken before enforcement of the regulations) keeping, transport, sale/exchange and offering for sale/exchange.
ECH5	Annex V of the European Communities Council Directive on the Conservation of Natural Habitats and Wild Fauna and Flora	Animal and plant species of community interest whose taking in the wild and exploitation may be subject to management measures.
PBA	Protection of Badgers Act 1992	Badgers are extensively protected by this Act, covering virtually any deliberate interference with the animals themselves or their setts.

---

[a] Annex I is concerned with habitats only and is therefore not included in this Checklist. Annex III is concerned with the criteria of conservation site selection. The Habitats Directive is enforced in Britain by The Conservation (Natural Habitats, &c.) Regulations 1994, amended in England by The Conservation (Natural Habitats, &c.) (Amendment) (England) Regulations 2000.

Code	Full Title	Explanation
WCA1i	Schedule 1 Part 1 of Wildlife and Countryside Act 1981 (and later Amendments)[b]	This Schedule lists birds protected by special penalties at all times, but virtually all wild birds have some protection in law. Acts which are prohibited for all wild birds (except derogated "pest" species - see text at start of Tables 4A and 4B) include intentional killing, injuring or taking; taking, damaging or destroying nests in use or being built; taking or destroying eggs; possessing or having control of (with certain exceptions but including live or dead birds, parts or derivatives); setting or permitting certain traps, weapons, decoys or poisons. Selling, offering or exposing for sale, possessing or transporting for sale any live wild bird[b], egg or part of an egg or advertising any of these for sale, or dead wild bird[c] including parts or derivatives are also prohibited. Many birds must be formally registered and ringed if kept in captivity. For WCA1i and 1ii (see below) Schedule birds, intentional or reckless disturbance while building a nest, or when such a bird is in, on or near a nest containing eggs or young, or intentional or reckless disturbance of dependent young, are all prohibited.
WCA1ii	Schedule 1 Part 2 of Wildlife and Countryside Act (including Amendments)	Birds protected by special penalties (as above) during close season.
WCA5	Schedule 5 of Wildlife and Countryside Act 1981 (and later Amendments)	Protected animals (other than birds). Acts which are prohibited include intentional killing, injuring or taking; possessing (including parts or derivatives); intentional or reckless damage, destruction or obstruction of any structure or place used for shelter or protection; selling, offering or exposing for sale, possessing or transporting for the purpose of sale (alive or dead, including parts or derivatives). *NB*. Protection of some species is limited to certain Sections of the Act which are indicated in the lists as follows: S9(1) — Protection limited to intentional killing, injury or taking. S9(2) — Protection limited to possessing/controlling any live or dead animal, or any part of, or anything derived from, such animal. S9(4a) — Protection limited to damaging, destroying, or obstructing access to, any structure or place used by the animal for shelter or protection. S9(4b) — Protection limited to disturbing the animal while it is occupying any structure or place which it uses for shelter or protection. S9(5) — Protection limited to selling, offering for sale, possessing or transporting for purpose of sale, or advertising for sale, any live or dead animal, or any part of, or anything derived from, such animal. Note that all cetaceans (whales and dolphins) and the basking shark (*Cetorhinus maximus*) are now protected from intentional or reckless disturbance.
WCA6	Schedule 6 of Wildlife and Countryside Act 1981 (and later Amendments)	Animals which may not be killed or taken by certain methods (traps and nets, poisons, automatic weapons, electrical devices, smokes/gases and various others). Even humane trapping for research requires a licence. Note that bows, explosives, self-locking snares and live bird or mammal decoys are generally prohibited for use against wild animals, irrespective of this Schedule.

[a] There are several other Schedules in this Act in addition to those included in the Checklist. They are concerned with close seasons, sale of birds, bird ringing, game species, release to the wild, import/export restrictions, interaction with related legislation, procedures and other matters beyond the scope of this Checklist.

[b] Except barn owl, blackbird, brambling, bullfinch, chaffinch, dunnock, goldfinch, greenfinch, jackdaw, jay, linnet, magpie, redpoll, reed bunting, siskin, song thrush, starling, twite and yellowhammer if ringed and bred in captivity.

[c] Except woodpigeon (at all times); capercaillie, common snipe, coot, golden plover, mallard, pintail, pochard, shoveler, teal, wigeon and woodcock (between 1 September and 28 February).

Code	Full Title	Explanation
WCA8	Schedule 8 of Wildlife and Countryside Act 1981 (and later Amendments)	Protected plants and fungi. Intentional picking, uprooting, destroying, trading (including parts or derivatives), *etc.* are prohibited. It should be noted that, under the Wildlife and Countryside Act, all wild plants in Britain are protected from intentional uprooting by an unauthorized person (but land owners, land occupiers, persons authorized by either of these, or persons authorized in writing by the Local Authority for the area are exempt). *NB.* Protection for some species may be limited to certain Sections of the Act and where this is the case it is indicated in the lists as follows: S13(2) Protection limited to selling, offering for sale, possessing or transporting for purpose of sale, or advertising for sale, any live or dead plant, or any part of, or anything derived from, such plant.

REMARKS ON THE COUNTRYSIDE AND RIGHTS OF WAY ACT 2000

The "CRoW Act" as it has rather unfortunately become known, received Royal Assent on 30 November 2000 and will have a major impact on matters relating to the countryside and wildlife in England and Wales (Scotland is planning separate but similar legislation). The Act, which is long and complex, is in five parts (Access, Rights of Way, Nature Conservation and Wildlife Protection, Areas of Outstanding Natural Beauty, and Town and Village Greens).

The CRoW Act is supplementary to the Wildlife and Countryside Act which it strengthens and updates. Matters relating to species will be found in the Act's Section 3: Nature Conservation and Wildlife Protection. For the first time there is a new statutory duty on English Government Departments and the National Assembly of Wales to have regard to biodiversity conservation in general and to maintain lists of species and habitats for which conservation steps should be taken or promoted. This places Biodiversity Action Plans (BAPs) within a statutory context and is aimed at enforcing the implementation of the principles of the Rio Biodiversity Convention which was signed as long ago as 1992.

The duty to list species of concern will give some added protection to such taxa, especially when they are in protected areas. However, inclusion in a BAP list does not confer legal protection *per se*: that remains the function of the schedules of the various legal instruments noted above. BAP species lists and local conservation measures generally are outside the intended scope of the Checklist.

The legal protection for wild fauna and flora species has been strengthened by the CroW Act in making some offences arrestable, with significantly increased search and seizure powers granted to the police. There is a new offence of "reckless disturbance" of a place of rest or shelter of a protected animal or a nest site (or any intentional or reckless disturbance of whales, dolphins and the basking shark). Further, almost all wildlife offences now have heavier fines and prison sentences.

To combat illegal trade, the police and wildlife inspectors have been given the power to enter premises to check species' sales controls and can require tissue samples to be taken from wildlife species for DNA analysis.

The whole text of the CroW Act is on the DETR web site (www.detr.gov.uk) and can be downloaded from there.

Cetorhinus maximus (Gunnerus) basking shark

PART A: PROTECTED SPECIES LISTED ALPHABETICALLY BY SCIENTIFIC NAME

TABLE 1A: INVERTEBRATES IN ALPHABETICAL ORDER OF SCIENTIFIC NAMES

Species	Common English name	Protection (see key at start of Tables)
Acosmetia caliginosa	reddish buff moth	WCA5
Aeshna isosceles	Norfolk aeshna dragonfly	WCA5
Alkmaria romijni	tentacled lagoon worm	WCA5
Apatura iris	purple emperor butterfly	WCA5(S9(5))
Argynnis adippe	high brown fritillary butterfly	WCA5
Aricia artaxerxes	northern brown argus butterfly	WCA5(S9(5))
Armandia cirrhosa	lagoon sandworm	WCA5
Astacus astacus	noble crayfish	BC3 ECH5 (see Table 8)
Atrina fragilis	fan mussel	WCA5(S9(1), S9(2), S9(5))
Austropotamobius pallipes	Atlantic stream crayfish	BC3 ECH2 WCA5(S9(1) taking only, S9(5))
Bembecia chrysidiformis	fiery clearwing moth	WCA5
Boloria euphrosyne	pearl-bordered fritillary butterfly	WCA5(S9(5))
Caecum armoricum	De Folin's lagoon snail	WCA5
Carterocephalus palaemon	checkered skipper butterfly	WCA5(S9(5))
Catinella arenaria	sandbowl snail	WCA5
Cerambyx cerdo	longhorn beetle	BC2 ECH2,4
Chirocephalus diaphanus	fairy shrimp	WCA5
Chrysolina cerealis	rainbow leaf beetle	WCA5
Cicadetta montana	New Forest cicada	WCA5
Clavopsella navis	marine hydroid	WCA5
Coenagrion mercuriale	southern damselfly	BC2 ECH2 WCA5
Coenonympha tullia	large heath butterfly	WCA5(S9(5))
Cupido minimus	small blue butterfly	WCA5(S9(5))
Curimopsis nigrita	mire pill beetle	WCA5(S9(4a))
Decticus verrucivorus	wart-biter grasshopper	WCA5
Dolomedes plantarius	fen raft spider	WCA5
Edwardsia ivelli	Ivell's sea-anemone	WCA5
Erebia epiphron	mountain ringlet butterfly	WCA5(S9(5))
Eresus niger	ladybird spider	WCA5

Species	Common English name	Protection (see key at start of Tables)
Eunicella verrucosa	pink sea-fan	WCA5(S9(1), S9(2), S9(5))
Euplagia quadripunctaria	Jersey tiger moth	ECH2
Eurodryas aurinia	marsh fritillary butterfly	WCA5
Gammarus insensibilis	lagoon sand shrimp	WCA5
Gortyna borelii	Fisher's estuarine moth	WCA5
Graphoderus bilineatus	water-beetle	BC2 ECH2,4
Graphoderus zonatus	water-beetle	WCA5
Gryllotalpa gryllotalpa	mole cricket	WCA5
Gryllus campestris	field cricket	WCA5
Hamearis lucina	Duke of Burgundy fritillary butterfly	WCA5(S9(5))
Helix pomatia	Roman snail	BC2 ECH2,4
Hesperia comma	silver-spotted skipper butterfly	WCA5(S9(5))
Hirudo medicinalis	medicinal leech	BC3 CITES2 ECH5 WCA5
Hydrochara caraboides	lesser silver water- beetle	WCA5
Hypebaeus flavipes	Moccas beetle	WCA5
Leptidea sinapis	wood white butterfly	WCA5(S9(5))
Limoniscus violaceus	violet click beetle	ECH2 WCA5
Lucanus cervus	stag beetle	BC3 ECH2 WCA5(S9(5))
Lycaena dispar	large copper butterfly	BC2 ECH2,4 WCA5
Lysandra bellargus	Adonis blue butterfly	WCA5(S9(5))
Lysandra coridon	chalkhill blue butterfly	WCA5(S9(5))
Maculinea arion	large blue butterfly	BC2 ECH4 WCA5
Margaritifera margaritifera	freshwater pearl mussel	BC3 ECH2,5 WCA5
Melicta athalia	heath fritillary butterfly	WCA5
Melitaea cinxia	Glanville fritillary butterfly	WCA5(S9(5))
Myxas glutinosa	glutinous snail	WCA5
Nematostella vectensis	starlet sea-anemone	WCA5
Nymphalis polychloros	large tortoiseshell butterfly	WCA5(S9(5))
Oxygastra curtesii	orange-spotted emerald dragonfly	BC2 ECH2,4
Paludinella littorina	lagoon snail	WCA5
Papilio machaon	swallowtail butterfly	WCA5
Paracymus aeneus	water-beetle	WCA5

Species	Common English name	Protection (see key at start of Tables)
Pareurlype berberata	barberry carpet moth	WCA5
Parnassius apollo	Apollo butterfly	CITES2 ECH4
Plebejus argus	silver-studded blue butterfly	WCA5(S9(5))
Proserpinus proserpina	Curzon's sphinx moth	BC2 ECH4
Siona lineata	black-veined moth	WCA5
Strymonidia pruni	black hairstreak butterfly	WCA5(S9(5))
Strymonidia w-album	white-letter hairstreak butterfly	WCA5(S9(5))
Tenellia adspersa	lagoon sea-slug	WCA5
Thalera fimbrialis	Sussex emerald moth	WCA5
Thecla betulae	brown hairstreak butterfly	WCA5(S9(5))
Thetida smaragdaria maritima	Essex emerald moth	WCA5
Thyasira gouldi	northern hatchet-snail	WCA5
Thymelicus acteon	Lulworth skipper butterfly	WCA5(S9(5))
Triops cancriformis	apus	WCA5
Vertigo angustior	land snail	ECH2
Vertigo genesii	land snail	ECH2
Vertigo geyeri	land snail	ECH2
Vertigo moulinsiana	Desmoulins' whorl snail	ECH2
Victorella pavida	trembling sea-mat	WCA5
Zygaena viciae argyllensis	New Forest burnet moth	WCA5

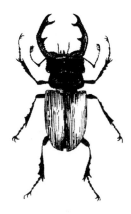

Lucanus cervus (L.)
stag beetle

TABLE 2A: FISH IN ALPHABETICAL ORDER OF SCIENTIFIC NAMES

Note there are various rules regarding fisheries and restrictions on season, methods, catches, *etc.* which are beyond the intended scope of the Checklist.

Species	Common English name	Protection (see key at start of Tables)
Acipenser sturio	sturgeon	BC2 CITES1 ECH2,4 WCA5
Alosa alosa	allis shad	BC3 ECH2,5 WCA5(S9(1), S9(4a))
Alosa fallax	twaite shad	BC3 ECH2,5 WCA5(S9(4a))
Barbus barbus	barbel	ECH5
Cetorhinus maximus	basking shark	WCA5 (see note in key)
Cobitis taenia	spined loach	BC3 ECH2
Coregonus albula	vendace	BC3 ECH5 WCA5
Coregonus lavaretus	powan	BC3 ECH5 WCA5
Coregonus oxyrinchus	houting	BC3 ECH[a]2,4
Cottus gobio	bullhead	ECH2
Gobius cobitis	giant goby	WCA5
Gobius couchii	Couch's goby	WCA5
Lampetra fluviatilis	river lamprey	BC3 ECH2,5
Lampetra planeri	brook lamprey	BC3 ECH2
Lota lota	burbot	WCA5
Petromyzon marinus	sea lamprey	BC3 ECH2
Pomatoschistus microps	common goby	BC3
Pomatoschistus minutus	sand goby	BC3
Rhodeus sericeus	bitterling	BC3 ECH2 (see Table 8)
Salmo salar	Atlantic salmon	BC3 ECH2,5 (only in fresh water)
Siluris glanis	wels	BC3 (see Table 8)
Thymallus thymallus	grayling	BC3 ECH5

Lampetra planeri (Bloch)
brook lamprey

[a] Only anadromous populations in certain sectors of the North Sea covered by ECH

TABLE 3A: AMPHIBIANS AND REPTILES IN ALPHABETICAL ORDER OF SCIENTIFIC NAMES

Species	Common English name	Protection (see key at start of Tables)
Alytes obstetricans	midwife toad	BC2 ECH4 (see Table 8)
Anguis fragilis	slow-worm	BC3 WCA5(S9(1) killing/injuring only, S9(5))
Bombina variegata	yellow-bellied toad	BC2 ECH2,4 (see Table 8)
Bufo bufo	common toad	BC3 WCA5(S9(5))
Bufo calamita	natterjack toad	BC2 ECH4 WCA5
Caretta caretta	loggerhead turtle	BC2 BoC1,2 CITES1 ECH2,4 WCA5
Chelonia mydas	green turtle	BC2 BoC1,2 CITES1 ECH4 WCA5
Coronella austriaca	smooth snake	BC2 ECH4 WCA5
Dermochelys coriacea	leatherback turtle	BC2 BoC1,2 CITES1 ECH4 WCA5
Elaphe longissima	Aesculapian snake	BC2 ECH4 (see Table 8)
Emys orbicularis	European pond terrapin	BC2 ECH2,4 (see Table 8)
Eretmochelys imbricata	hawk's-bill turtle	BC2 BoC1,2 CITES1 ECH4 WCA5
Hyla arborea	European tree frog	BC2 ECH4 (see Table 8)
Lacerta agilis	sand lizard	BC2 ECH4 WCA5
Lacerta vivipara	common lizard	BC3 WCA5(S9(1) killing/injuring only, S9(5))
Lepidochelys kempii	Kemp's ridley turtle	BC2 BoC1,2 CITES1 ECH4 WCA5
Natrix natrix	grass snake	BC3 WCA5(S9(1) killing/injuring only, S9(5))
Podarcis muralis	common wall lizard	BC2 ECH4
Rana esculenta	edible frog	BC3 ECH5
Rana lessonae	pool frog	BC3 ECH4
Rana ridibunda	marsh frog	BC3 ECH5 (see Table 8)
Rana temporaria	common frog	BC3 WCA5(S9(5))
Triturus alpestris	alpine newt	BC3 (see Table 8)
Triturus cristatus carnifex	Italian crested newt	BC2 ECH2,4 (see Table 8)
Triturus cristatus cristatus	great crested newt	BC2 ECH2,4 WCA5
Triturus helveticus	palmate newt	BC3 WCA5(S9(5))
Triturus vulgaris	smooth newt	BC3 WCA5(S9(5))
Vipera berus	adder	BC3 WCA5(S9(1) killing/injuring only, S9(5))

TABLE 4A: BIRDS IN ALPHABETICAL ORDER OF SCIENTIFIC NAMES

With the exception of 13 very abundant or pest species (great and lesser black-backed gull, herring gull, wood pigeon, house sparrow, starling, jay, magpie, carrion crow, rook, jackdaw, feral pigeon and collared dove) which may be killed by authorized persons, the Wildlife and Countryside Act gives general protection to **all** wild birds in Britain from killing, injuring or taking as well as taking, damaging or destroying nests in use or being built, and taking or destroying eggs. Only birds which have special protection under the Wildlife and Countryside Act are listed in this Table. Appendix III of the Berne Convention includes all birds not listed in Appendix II except 11 abundant/pest species (great and lesser black-backed gull, herring gull, wood pigeon, house sparrow, starling, jay, magpie, carrion crow, rook, jackdaw). Berne Convention Appendix III has therefore been ignored for the purposes of this Checklist but readers should nonetheless take note of its existence. With regard to the EC Birds Directive, only species on the Directive's specially protected Annex I list are included in the Checklist. Birds only required to be registered and ringed if kept in captivity (WCA Schedule 4) are also excluded as are game birds (which have particular rules) not enjoying **special** protection in the close season. Birds on Bonn Convention Appendix II only appear in this Checklist if they are listed under other instruments. Please also note the Bonn Convention Agreement protecting African-Eurasian migratory waterbirds which includes, *inter alia*, all the **Anatidae**.

Many species of birds are only occasional visitors to Britain and it has been difficult to decide which of these to include. Please therefore note that some protected species which are recorded only very rarely as vagrants to Britain are excluded from this Checklist.

Species	Common English name	Protection (see key at start of Tables)
Accipiter gentilis	goshawk	BC2 BoC2 WCA1i
Accipiter nisus	sparrowhawk	BC2 BoC2
Acrocephalus palustris	marsh warbler	BC2 WCA1i
Acrocephalus schoenobaenus	sedge warbler	BC2
Acrocephalus scirpaceus	reed warbler	BC2
Aegithalos caudatus	long-tailed tit	BC2
Alcedo atthis	kingfisher	BC2 ECB WCA1i
Anas acuta	pintail	BoC2 CITES3 WCA1ii
Anas formosa	Baikal teal	BoC2 CITES2
Anas querquedula	garganey	BoC2 CITES3 WCA1i
Anser albifrons flavirostris	white-fronted goose (Greenland race)	BoC2 ECB
Anser anser	greylag goose	BoC2 WCA1ii (restricted areas)
Anthus petrosus	rock pipit	BC2
Anthus pratensis	meadow pipit	BC2
Anthus spinoletta	water pipit	BC2
Anthus trivialis	tree pipit	BC2
Apus melba	alpine swift	BC2
Apus pallida	pallid swift	BC2
Aquila chrysaetos	golden eagle	BC2 BoC2 ECB WCA1i
Ardea purpurea	purple heron	BC2 BoC2 (if breeding) ECB WCA1i
Ardeola ralloides	squacco heron	BC2 ECB

BIRDS - SCIENTIFIC NAMES

Species	Common English name	Protection (see key at start of Tables)
Arenaria interpres	turnstone	BC2 BoC2
Asio flammeus	short-eared owl	BC2 CITES2 ECB
Asio otus	long-eared owl	BC2 CITES2
Athene noctua	little owl	BC2 CITES2
Aythya marila	scaup	BoC2 WCA1i
Bombycilla garrulus	waxwing	BC2
Botaurus stellaris	bittern	BC2 BoC2 ECB WCA1i
Branta leucopsis	barnacle goose	BC2 BoC2 ECB
Branta ruficollis	red-breasted goose	BC2 BoC2 CITES2 ECB
Bubulcus ibis	cattle egret	BC2 CITES3
Bucephala clangula	goldeneye	ECB BoC2 WCA1ii
Burhinus oedicnemus	stone curlew	BC2 BoC2 ECB WCA1i
Buteo buteo	buzzard	BC2 BoC2
Buteo lagopus	rough-legged buzzard	BC2 BoC2
Calcarius lapponicus	Lapland bunting	BC2 WCA1i
Calidris alba	sanderling	BC2 BoC2
Calidris alpina	dunlin	BC2 BoC2
Calidris ferruginea	curlew sandpiper	BC2 BoC2
Calidris maritima	purple sandpiper	BC2 BoC2 WCA1i
Calidris minuta	little stint	BC2 BoC2
Calidris temminckii	Teminck's stint	BC2 BoC2 WCA1i
Caprimulgus aegyptius	Egyptian nightjar	BC2
Caprimulgus europaeus	nightjar	BC2 ECB
Caprimulgus ruficollis	red-necked nightjar	BC2
Carduelis cannabina	linnet	BC2
Carduelis carduelis	goldfinch	BC2
Carduelis chloris	greenfinch	BC2
Carduelis flammea	redpoll	BC2
Carduelis flavirostris	twite	BC2
Carduelis spinus	siskin	BC2
Carpodacus erythrinus	scarlet rosefinch	BC2 WCA1i
Certhia brachydactyla	short-toed treecreeper	BC2 WCA1i

VERSION 02.2/CBEB 0501

Species	Common English name	Protection (see key at start of Tables)
Certhia familiaris	treecreeper	BC2
Cettia cetti	Cetti's warbler	BC2 WCA1i
Charadrius alexandrinus	Kentish plover	BC2 BoC2 WCA1i
Charadrius dubius	little ringed plover	BC2 BoC2 WCA1i
Charadrius hiaticula	ringed plover	BC2 BoC2
Charadrius morinellus	dotterel	BC2 BoC2 ECB WCA1i
Chlidonias hybridus	whiskered tern	BC2 ECB
Chlidonias niger	black tern	BC2 BoC2 ECB WCA1i
Ciconia ciconia	white stork	BC2 BoC2 ECB
Ciconia nigra	black stork	BC2 BoC2 CITES2 ECB
Cinclus cinclus	dipper	BC2
Circus aeruginosus	marsh harrier	BC2 BoC2 ECB WCA1i
Circus cyaneus	hen harrier	BC2 BoC2 ECB WCA1i
Circus pygargus	Montagu's harrier	BC2 BoC2 ECB WCA1i
Cisticola juncidis	fan-tailed warbler	BC2
Clangula hyemalis	long-tailed duck	BoC2 WCA1i
Coccothraustes coccothraustes	hawfinch	BC2
Coracias garrulus	roller	BC2 BoC2 ECB
Coturnix coturnix	common quail	BoC2 WCA1i
Crex crex	corncrake	BC2 ECB WCA1i
Cursorius cursor	cream-coloured courser	BC2 ECB
Cygnus columbianus bewickii	Bewick's swan	BC2 BoC2 ECB WCA1i
Cygnus cygnus	whooper swan	BC2 BoC2 ECB WCA1i
Delichon urbica	house martin	BC2
Dendrocopos major	great spotted woodpecker	BC2
Dendrocopos minor	lesser spotted woodpecker	BC2
Egretta alba	great white egret	BC2 CITES3 ECB
Egretta garzetta	little egret	BC2 CITES3 ECB
Emberiza cirlus	cirl bunting	BC2 WCA1i
Emberiza citrinella	yellowhammer	BC2
Emberiza schoeniclus	reed bunting	BC2
Eremophila alpestris	shore lark	BC2 WCA1i

Species	Common English name	Protection (see key at start of Tables)
Erithacus rubecula	robin	BC2
Falco columbarius	merlin	BC2 BoC2 CITES2 ECB WCA1i
Falco peregrinus	peregrine	BC2 BoC2 CITES1 ECB WCA1i
Falco rusticolus	gyrfalcon	BC2 BoC2 CITES1 ECB WCA1i
Falco subbuteo	hobby	BC2 BoC2 CITES2 WCA1i
Falco tinnunculus	kestrel	BC2 BoC2 CITES2
Ficedula hypoleuca	pied flycatcher	BC2 BoC2
Fringilla montifringilla	brambling	WCA1i
Gallinago media	great snipe	BC2 BoC2 ECB
Gavia adamsii	white-billed diver	BC2 BoC2 WCA1i
Gavia arctica	black-throated diver	BC2 BoC2 ECB WCA1i
Gavia immer	great northern diver	BC2 BoC2 ECB WCA1i
Gavia stellata	red-throated diver	BC2 BoC2 ECB WCA1i
Gelochelidon nilotica	gull-billed tern	BC2 ECB
Glareola pratincola	collared pratincole	BC2 BoC2 ECB
Grus grus	common crane	BC2 BoC2 CITES2 ECB
Haliaeetus albicilla	white-tailed eagle	BC2 BoC1,2 CITES1 ECB WCA1i
Himantopus himantopus	black-winged stilt	BC2 BoC2 ECB WCA1i
Hirundo riparia	sand martin	BC2
Hirundo rustica	swallow	BC2
Histrionicus histrionicus	harlequin duck	BC2 BoC2
Hydrobates pelagicus	storm petrel	BC2 ECB
Ixobrychus minutus	little bittern	BC2 BoC2 ECB WCA1i
Jynx torquilla	wryneck	BC2 WCA1i
Lanius collurio	red-backed shrike	BC2 ECB WCA1i
Lanius excubitor	great grey shrike	BC2
Larus genei	slender-billed gull	BC2 BoC2 ECB
Larus melanocephalus	Mediterranean gull	BC2 BoC2 ECB WCA1i
Larus minutus	little gull	BC2 WCA1i
Larus sabini	Sabine's gull	BC2
Limosa limosa	black-tailed godwit	BoC2 WCA1i
Locustella luscinioides	Savi's warbler	BC2 WCA1i

VERSION 02.2/CBEB 0501

Species	Common English name	Protection (see key at start of Tables)
Locustella naevia	grasshopper warbler	BC2
Loxia curvirostra	crossbill	BC2 WCA1i
Loxia leucoptera	two-barred crossbill	BC2 WCA1i
Loxia pytyopsittacus	parrot crossbill	BC2 WCA1i
Loxia scotica	Scottish crossbill	BC2 ECB WCA1i
Lullula arborea	wood lark	ECB WCA1i
Luscinia megarhynchos	nightingale	BC2
Luscinia svecica	bluethroat	BC2 ECB WCA1i
Melanitta fusca	velvet scoter	BoC2 WCA1i
Melanitta nigra	common scoter	BoC2 WCA1i
Mergus albellus	smew	BC2 BoC2
Merops apiaster	bee-eater	BC2 BoC2 WCA1i
Milvus migrans	black kite	BC2 BoC2 ECB
Milvus milvus	red kite	BC2 BoC2 ECB WCA1i
Motacilla alba	pied wagtail	BC2
Motacilla cinerea	grey wagtail	BC2
Motacilla flava	yellow wagtail	BC2
Muscicapa striata	spotted flycatcher	BC2 BoC2
Numenius phaeopus	whimbrel	BoC2 WCA1i
Nyctea scandiaca	snowy owl	BC2 ECB CITES2 WCA1i
Nycticorax nycticorax	night heron	BC2 ECB
Oceanodroma leucorhoa	Leach's petrel	BC2 ECB WCA1i
Oenanthe oenanthe	wheatear	BC2
Oriolus oriolus	golden oriole	BC2 WCA1i
Pandion haliaetus	osprey	BC2 BoC2 ECB WCA1i
Panurus biarmicus	bearded reedling	BC2 WCA1i
Parus ater	coal tit	BC2
Parus caeruleus	blue tit	BC2
Parus cristatus	crested tit	BC2 WCA1i
Parus major	great tit	BC2
Parus montanus	willow tit	BC2
Parus palustris	marsh tit	BC2

Species	Common English name	Protection (see key at start of Tables)
Pernis apivorus	honey buzzard	BC2 BoC2 ECB WCA1i
Phalaropus fulicarius	grey phalarope	BC2 BoC2
Phalaropus lobatus	red-necked phalarope	BC2 BoC2 ECB WCA1i
Phalaropus tricolor	Wilson's phalarope	BC2 BoC2
Philomachus pugnax	ruff	BoC2 ECB WCA1i
Phoenicurus ochruros	black redstart	BC2 WCA1i
Phoenicurus phoenicurus	redstart	BC2
Phylloscopus collybita	chiffchaff	BC2
Phylloscopus sibilatrix	wood warbler	BC2
Phylloscopus trochilus	willow warbler	BC2
Picus viridis	green woodpecker	BC2
Platalea leucorodia	spoonbill	BC2 BoC2 CITES2 ECB WCA1i
Plectrophenax nivalis	snow bunting	BC2 WCA1i
Plegadis falcinellus	glossy ibis	BC2 BoC2 ECB
Pluvialis apricaria	golden plover	BoC2 ECB (exceptions outside close season)
Podiceps auritus	Slavonian grebe	BC2 BoC2 ECB WCA1i
Podiceps grisegena	red-necked grebe	BC2 BoC2
Podiceps nigricollis	black-necked grebe	BC2 WCA1i
Podiceps ruficollis	little grebe	BC2
Porzana porzana	spotted crake	BC2 BoC2 ECB WCA1i
Prunella modularis	dunnock	BC2
Puffinus puffinus	Manx shearwater	BC2
Pyrrhocorax pyrrhocorax	chough	BC2 ECB WCA1i
Recurvirostra avocetta	avocet	BC2 BoC2 ECB WCA1i
Regulus ignicapillus	firecrest	BC2 WCA1i
Regulus regulus	goldcrest	BC2
Saxicola rubetra	whinchat	BC2
Saxicola torquata	stonechat	BC2
Serinus serinus	serin	BC2 WCA1i
Sitta europaea	nuthatch	BC2
Sterna albifrons	little tern	BC2 BoC2 ECB WCA1i
Sterna caspia	Caspian tern	BC2 BoC2 ECB

Species	Common English name	Protection (see key at start of Tables)
Sterna dougallii	roseate tern	BC2 BoC2 ECB WCA1i
Sterna hirundo	common tern	BC2 BoC2 ECB
Sterna paradisaea	arctic tern	BC2 BoC2 ECB
Sterna sandvicensis	Sandwich tern	BC2 BoC2 ECB
Strix aluco	tawny owl	BC2 CITES2
Sylvia atricapilla	blackcap	BC2
Sylvia borin	garden warbler	BC2
Sylvia communis	common whitethroat	BC2
Sylvia curruca	lesser whitethroat	BC2
Sylvia undata	Dartford warbler	BC2 ECB WCA1i
Syrrhaptes paradoxus	Pallas' sandgrouse	BC2
Tadorna ferruginea	ruddy shelduck	BC2 BoC2 ECB
Tadorna tadorna	common shelduck	BC2 BoC2
Tetrao urogallus	capercaillie	ECB (exceptions outside close season; voluntary ban on shooting)
Tringa glareola	wood sandpiper	BC2 BoC2 ECB WCA1i
Tringa hypoleucos	common sandpiper	BC2 BoC2
Tringa nebularia	greenshank	BoC2 WCA1i
Tringa ochropus	green sandpiper	BC2 BoC2 WCA1i
Troglodytes troglodytes	wren	BC2
Turdus iliacus	redwing	WCA1i
Turdus pilaris	fieldfare	WCA1i
Tyto alba	barn owl	BC2 CITES2 WCA1i
Upupa epops	hoopoe	BC2 WCA1i

Circus aeruginosus
marsh harrier

TABLE 5A: MAMMALS IN ALPHABETICAL ORDER OF SCIENTIFIC NAMES

Only limited conservation protection is afforded to some mammals below (but see Note at end of this Table regarding cruelty). Note that ALL cetaceans (whales and dolphins) are protected from any intentional or reckless disturbance.

Species	Common English name	Protection (see key at start of Tables)
Arvicola terrestris	water vole	WCA5(S9(4a, 4b))
Balaenoptera acutorostrata	minke whale	BC3 CITES1 ECH4 WCA5
Balaenoptera borealis	sei whale	BC3 CITES1 ECH4 WCA5
Balaenoptera musculus	blue whale	BC3 BoC1 CITES1 ECH4 WCA5
Balaenoptera physalus	fin whale	BC2 CITES1 ECH4 WCA5
Barbastella barbastellus	barbastelle	BC2 BoC2 ECH2,4 WCA5,6
Capreolus capreolus	roe deer	BC3 DA DSA
Cervus elaphus	red deer	BC3 DA DSA (see also Table 8)
Cervus nippon	sika deer	BC3 DA DSA (see also Table 8)
Crocidura suaveolens	lesser white-toothed shrew	BC3 WCA6
Cystophora cristata	hooded seal	BC3 CSA (partial) ECH5
Dama dama	fallow deer	BC3 DA DSA
Delphinapterus leucas	white whale	BC3 BoC2 CITES2 ECH4 WCA5
Delphinus delphis	common dolphin	BC2 BoC2 CITES2 ECH4 WCA5,6
Eptesicus serotinus	serotine	BC2 BoC2 ECH4 WCA5,6
Erignathus barbatus	bearded seal	BC3 CSA (partial) ECH5
Erinaceus europaeus	hedgehog	BC3 WCA6
Eubalaena glacialis	northern right whale	BC2 BoC1 CITES1 ECH4 WCA5
Felis silvestris	wild cat	BC2 ECH4 CITES2 WCA5,6
Glis glis	edible dormouse	BC3 WCA6
Globicephala melas	long-finned pilot whale	BC2 BoC2 CITES2 ECH4 WCA5
Grampus griseus	Risso's dolphin	BC2 BoC2 CITES2 ECH4 WCA5
Halichoerus grypus	grey seal	BC3 CSA ECH2
Hydropotes inermis	water deer	BC3 DA DSA
Hyperoodon ampullatus	northern bottlenose whale	BC3 BoC2 CITES1 ECH4 WCA5
Kogia breviceps	pygmy sperm whale	BC2 CITES2 ECH4 WCA5
Lagenorhynchus acutus	Atlantic white-sided dolphin	BC2 BoC2 CITES2 ECH4 WCA5

Species	Common English name	Protection (see key at start of Tables)
Lagenorhynchus albirostris	white-beaked dolphin	BC2 BoC2 CITES2 ECH4 WCA5
Lepus timidus	mountain hare	BC3 ECH5
Lutra lutra	otter	BC2 ECH2,4 CITES1 WCA5,6
Martes martes	pine marten	BC3 ECH5 WCA5,6
Megaptera novaeangliae	humpback whale	BC2 BoC1 CITES1 ECH4 WCA5
Meles meles	badger	BC3 PBA WCA6
Mesoplodon bidens	Sowerby's beaked whale	BC2 CITES2 ECH4 WCA5
Mesoplodon europaeus	Gervais' beaked whale	BC3 CITES2 ECH4 WCA5
Mesoplodon mirus	True's beaked whale	BC2 CITES2 ECH4 WCA5
Monodon monoceros	narwhal	BC2 BoC2 CITES2 ECH4 WCA5
Muntiacus reevesii	muntjac	BC3 DA DSA[a]
Muscardinus avellanarius	common dormouse	BC3 ECH4 WCA5,6
Mustela erminea	stoat	BC3
Mustela nivalis	weasel	BC3
Mustela putorius	polecat	BC3 ECH5 WCA6
Myotis bechsteinii	Bechstein's bat	BC2 BoC2 ECH2,4 WCA5,6
Myotis brandtii	Brandt's bat	BC2 BoC2 ECH4 WCA5,6
Myotis daubentonii	Daubenton's bat	BC2 BoC2 ECH4 WCA5,6
Myotis myotis	mouse-eared bat	BC2 BoC2 ECH2,4 WCA5,6
Myotis mystacinus	whiskered bat	BC2 BoC2 ECH4 WCA5,6
Myotis nattereri	Natterer's bat	BC2 BoC2 ECH4 WCA5,6
Neomys fodiens	water shrew	BC3 WCA6
Nyctalus leisleri	Leisler's bat	BC2 BoC2 ECH4 WCA5,6
Nyctalus noctula	noctule	BC2 BoC2 ECH4 WCA5,6
Odobenus rosmarus	walrus	BC2 CITES3 WCA5
Orcinus orca	killer whale	BC2 BoC2 CITES2 ECH4 WCA5
Phoca groenlandica	harp seal	BC3 CSA (partial) ECH5
Phoca vitulina	common seal	BC3 CSA ECH2
Phocoena phocoena	harbour porpoise	BC2 BoC2 CITES2 ECH2,4 WCA5,6
Physeter macrocephalus	sperm whale	BC3 CITES1 ECH4 WCA5

[a] Unlikely to be found in Scotland, but spreading.

Species	Common English name	Protection (see key at start of Tables)
Pipistrellus pipistrellus[a]	pipistrelle	BC3 BoC2 ECH4 WCA5,6
Plecotus auritus	brown long-eared bat	BC2 BoC2 ECH4 WCA5,6
Plecotus austriacus	grey long-eared bat	BC2 BoC2 ECH4 WCA5,6
Pseudorca crassidens	false killer whale	BC2 CITES2 ECH4 WCA5
Rangifer tarandus[b]	reindeer	BC3 DA DSA
Rhinolophus ferrumequinum	greater horseshoe bat	BC2 BoC2 ECH2,4 WCA5,6
Rhinolophus hipposideros	lesser horseshoe bat	BC2 BoC2 ECH2,4 WCA5,6
Sciurus vulgaris	red squirrel	BC3 WCA5,6
Sorex araneus	common shrew	BC3 WCA6
Sorex minutus	pygmy shrew	BC3 WCA6
Stenella coeruleoalba	striped dolphin	BC2 (BoC2)[c] CITES2 ECH4 WCA5
Tursiops truncatus	bottle-nosed dolphin	BC2 BoC2 CITES2 ECH2,4 WCA5,6
Ziphius cavirostris	Cuvier's beaked whale	BC2 CITES2 ECH4 WCA5

Note: The Wild Mammals (Protection) Act was passed in 1996. With certain exceptions such as lawful hunting, vermin trapping and humane destruction, this legislation makes it an offence to mutilate, kick, beat, impale, stab, burn, stone, crush, drown, drag or asphyxiate any wild mammal with intent to inflict unnecessary suffering.

Felis silvestris Schreber
wild cat

---

[a] Now believed to be two closely related spp.

[b] Extinct in wild but free-ranging managed herd in Cairngorms

[c] Occasional visitor to British waters - the Western Mediterranean population of *S. coeruleoalba* is on BoC2

VERSION 02.2/CBEB 0501

TABLE 6A: ALGAE, LICHENS, BRYOPHYTES, STONEWORTS (NON-VASCULAR PLANTS) AND FUNGI IN ALPHABETICAL ORDER OF SCIENTIFIC NAMES

Protected species include any subspecies or varieties - these are not listed separately in the Table.

Species	Common English name	Protection (see key at start of Tables)
Acaulon triquetrum	triangular pygmy-moss	WCA8
Adelanthus lindenbergianus	Lindenberg's leafy liverwort	WCA8
Alectoria ochroleuca	alpine sulphur-tresses	WCA8
Anomodon longifolius	long-leaved anomodon	WCA8
Barbula cordata	cordate beard-moss	WCA8
Barbula glauca	glaucous braer-moss	WCA8
Bartramia stricta	rigid apple-moss	WCA8
Battarraea phalloides	sandy stilt puffball	WCA8
Boletus regius	royal bolete	WCA8
Bryoria furcellata	forked hair-lichen	WCA8
Bryum mamillatum	dune thread-moss	WCA8
Bryum neodamense	long-leaved thread-moss	WCA8
Bryum schleicheri var. latifolium	Schleicher's thread-moss	WCA8
Buglossoporus pulvinus	oak polypore	WCA8
Buellia asterella	starry breck-lichen	WCA8
Buxbaumia viridis	green shield-moss	BC1 ECH2 WCA8
Caloplaca luteoalba	orange-fruited elm-lichen	WCA8
Caloplaca nivalis	snow caloplaca	WCA8
Catapyrenium psoromoides	tree catapyrenium	WCA8
Catillaria laureri	Laurer's catillaria	WCA8
Catolechia wahlenbergii	goblin-lights	WCA8
Chara canescens	bearded stonewort	WCA8
Cladonia arbuscula (subgen. *Cladina*)	reindeer lichen	ECH5
Cladonia ciliata (subgen. *Cladina*)	reindeer lichen	ECH5
Cladonia convoluta	convoluted cladonia (reindeer lichen)	WCA8
Cladonia mediterranea (subgen. *Cladina*)	reindeer lichen	ECH5
Cladonia mitis (subgen. *Cladina*)	reindeer lichen	ECH5
Cladonia portentosa (subgen. *Cladina*)	reindeer lichen	ECH5

Species	Common English name	Protection (see key at start of Tables)
Cladonia rangiferina (subgen. *Cladina*)	reindeer lichen	ECH5
Cladonia stellaris (subgen. *Cladina*)	reindeer lichen	ECH5
Cladonia stricta	upright mountain cladonia (reindeer lichen)	WCA8
Cladonia stygia (subgen. *Cladina*)	reindeer lichen	ECH5
Collema dichotomum	river jelly lichen	WCA8
Cryphaea lamyana	multi-fruited river-moss	WCA8
Cyclodictyon laetevirens	bright green cave-moss	WCA8
Desmatodon cernuus	flamingo moss	WCA8
Ditrichum cornubicum	Cornish path-moss	WCA8
Drepanocladus vernicosus	slender green feather-moss	BC1 ECH2 WCA8
Enterographa elaborata	New Forest beech-lichen	WCA8
Geocalyx graveolens	turpswort	WCA8
Grimmia unicolor	blunt-leaved grimmia	WCA8
Gyalecta ulmi	elm gyalecta	WCA8
Gymnomitrion apiculatum	pointed frostwort	WCA8
Hericium erinaceum	hedgehog fungus	WCA8
Heterodermia leucomelos	ciliate strap-lichen	WCA8
Heterodermia propagulifera	coralloid rosette-lichen	WCA8
Hygrohypnum polare	Polar feather-moss	WCA8
Hypnum vaucheri	Vaucher's feather-moss	WCA8
Jamesoniella undulifolia	marsh earwort	WCA8
Lamprothamnium papulosum	foxtail stonewort	WCA8
Lecanactis hemisphaerica	churchyard lecanactis	WCA8
Lecanora achariana	tarn lecanora	WCA8
Lecidea inops	copper lecidea	WCA8
Leiocolea rutheana	Norfolk flapwort	WCA8
Leucobryum glaucum	dryad's cushion	ECH5
Lithothamnium corallioides	maerl (a coralline red alga)	ECH5
Marsupella profunda	western rustwort	BC1 ECH2 WCA8
Micromitrium tenerum	millimetre moss	WCA8
Mielichhoferia mielichhoferi	alpine copper-moss	WCA8
Nephroma arcticum	arctic kidney-lichen	WCA8

Species	Common English name	Protection (see key at start of Tables)
Orthotrichum obtusifolium	blunt-leaved bristle-moss	WCA8
Pannaria ignobilis	Caledonia pannaria	WCA8
Parmelia minarum	New Forest parmelia	WCA8
Parmentaria chilensis	oil-stain parmentaria	WCA8
Peltigera lepidophora	ear-lobed dog-lichen	WCA8
Pertusaria bryontha	alpine moss pertusaria	WCA8
Petalophyllum ralfsii	petalwort	BC1 ECH2 WCA8
Phymatolithon calcareum	maerl (a coralline red alga)	ECH5
Physcia tribacioides	southern grey physcia	WCA8
Plagiothecium piliferum	hair silk-moss	WCA8
Pseudocyphellaria lacerata	ragged pseudocyphellaria	WCA8
Psora rubiformis	rusty alpine psora	WCA8
Rhynchostegium rotundifolium	round-leaved feather-moss	WCA8
Riccia bifurca	Lizard crystalwort	WCA8
Saelania glaucescens	blue dew-moss	WCA8
Scorpidium turgescens	large yellow feather-moss	WCA8
Solenopsora liparina	serpentine solenopsora	WCA8
Southbya nigrella	blackwort	WCA8
Sphagnum auriculatum	cow-horn bog moss	ECH5
Sphagnum balticum	Baltic bog moss	ECH5 WCA8
Sphagnum capillifolium	red bog moss	ECH5
Sphagnum compactum	compact bog moss	ECH5
Sphagnum contortum	twisted bog moss	ECH5
Sphagnum cuspidatum	feathery bog moss	ECH5
Sphagnum fimbriatum	fringed bog moss	ECH5
Sphagnum fuscum	rusty bog moss	ECH5
Sphagnum girgensohnii	Girgensohn's bog moss	ECH5
Sphagnum imbricatum	Austin's bog moss	ECH5
Sphagnum lindbergii	Lindberg's bog moss	ECH5
Sphagnum magellanicum	Magellanic bog moss	ECH5
Sphagnum majus	olive bog moss	ECH5
Sphagnum molle	blushing bog moss	ECH5

Species	Common English name	Protection (see key at start of Tables)
Sphagnum obtusum	obtuse bog moss	ECH5
Sphagnum palustre	blunt-leaved bog moss	ECH5
Sphagnum papillosum	papillose bog moss	ECH5
Sphagnum platyphyllum	flat-leaved bog moss	ECH5
Sphagnum pulchrum	golden bog moss	ECH5
Sphagnum quinquefarium	five-ranked bog moss	ECH5
Sphagnum recurvum	flexuous bog moss	ECH5
Sphagnum riparium	cleft bog moss	ECH5
Sphagnum russowii	Russow's bog moss	ECH5
Sphagnum squarrosum	spiky bog moss	ECH5
Sphagnum strictum	pale bog moss	ECH5
Sphagnum subnitens	lustrous bog moss	ECH5
Sphagnum subsecundum	slender cow-horn bog moss	ECH5
Sphagnum tenellum	soft bog moss	ECH5
Sphagnum teres	rigid bog moss	ECH5
Sphagnum warnstorfii	Warnstorf's bog moss	ECH5
Squamarina lentigera	scaly breck-lichen	WCA8
Teloschistes flavicans	golden hair-lichen	WCA8
Thamnobryum angustifolium	Derbyshire feather-moss	WCA8
Zygodon forsteri	knothole moss	WCA8
Zygodon gracilis	Nowell's limestone moss	WCA8

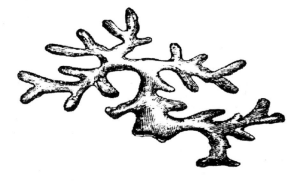

Phymatolithon calcareum (Pall.) Adey & McKibb.
maerl

TABLE 7A: TRACHEOPHYTES (VASCULAR PLANTS) IN ALPHABETICAL ORDER OF SCIENTIFIC NAMES

Protected species include any subspecies or varieties and, in the *Orchidaceae* (orchids) interspecific and intergeneric hybrids - these are not listed separately in the Table. Parts and derivatives are also included.

Species	Common English name	Protection (see key at start of Tables)
Aceras anthropophorum	man orchid	CITES2
Ajuga chamaepitys	ground-pine	WCA8
Alisma gramineum	ribbon-leaved water-plantain	WCA8
Allium sphaerocephalon	round-headed leek	WCA8
Althaea hirsuta	rough marsh-mallow	WCA8
Alyssum alyssoides	small alison	WCA8
Anacamptis pyramidalis	pyramidal orchid	CITES2
Apium repens	creeping marshwort	BC1 ECH2,4 WCA8
Arabis alpina	alpine rock-cress	WCA8
Arabis stricta	Bristol rock-cress	WCA8
Arenaria norvegica	Norwegian sandwort	WCA8
Artemisia campestris	field wormwood	WCA8
Bromus interruptus	interrupted brome	BC1
Bupleurum baldense	small hare's-ear	WCA8
Bupleurum falcatum	sickle-leaved hare's-ear	WCA8
Calamintha sylvatica	wood calamint	WCA8
Carex depauperata	starved wood-sedge	WCA8
Centaurium tenuiflorum	slender centaury	WCA8
Cephalanthera damasonium	white helleborine	CITES2
Cephalanthera longifolia	narrow-leaved helleborine	CITES2
Cephalanthera rubra	red helleborine	CITES2 WCA8
Chenopodium vulvaria	stinking goosefoot	WCA8
Cicerbita alpina	alpine blue-sow-thistle	WCA8
Coeloglossum viride	frog orchid	CITES2
Corallorrhiza trifida	coralroot orchid	CITES2
Corrigiola litoralis	strapwort	WCA8
Cotoneaster integerrimus	wild cotoneaster	WCA8
Crassula aquatica	pigmyweed	WCA8
Crepis foetida	stinking hawk's-beard	WCA8

Species	Common English name	Protection (see key at start of Tables)
Cynoglossum germanicum	green hound's-tongue	WCA8
Cyperus fuscus	brown galingale	WCA8
Cypripedium calceolus	lady's-slipper	BC1 CITES2 ECH2,4 WCA8
Cystopteris dickieana	Dickie's bladder fern	WCA8
Dactylorhiza fuchsii	common spotted-orchid	CITES2
Dactylorhiza incarnata	early marsh-orchid	CITES2
Dactylorhiza lapponica	Lapland marsh-orchid	CITES2 WCA8
Dactylorhiza maculata	heath spotted-orchid	CITES2
Dactylorhiza majalis	western marsh-orchid	CITES2
Dactylorhiza praetermissa	southern marsh-orchid	CITES2
Dactylorhiza purpurella	northern marsh-orchid	CITES2
Dactylorhiza traunsteineri	narrow-leaved marsh-orchid	CITES2
Damasonium alisma	starfruit	WCA8
Dianthus armeria	Deptford pink	WCA8 (England & Wales only)
Dianthus gratianopolitanus	Cheddar pink	WCA8
Diapensia lapponica	diapensia	WCA8
Diphasiastrum alpinum	alpine clubmoss	ECH5
Diphasiastrum complanatum	Issler's clubmoss	ECH5
Eleocharis parvula	dwarf spike-rush	WCA8
Epipactis atrorubens	dark-red helleborine	CITES2
Epipactis helleborine	broad-leaved helleborine	CITES2
Epipactis leptochila	narrow-lipped helleborine	CITES2
Epipactis palustris	marsh helleborine	CITES2
Epipactis phyllanthes	green-flowered helleborine	CITES2
Epipactis purpurata	violet helleborine	CITES2
Epipactis youngiana	Young's helleborine	CITES2 WCA8
Epipogium aphyllum	ghost orchid	CITES2 WCA8
Equisetum ramosissimum	branched horsetail	WCA8
Erigeron borealis	alpine fleabane	WCA8
Eriophorum gracile	slender cottongrass	WCA8
Eryngium campestre	field eryngo	WCA8
Filago lutescens	red-tipped cudweed	WCA8

VERSION 02.2/CBEB 0501

Species	Common English name	Protection (see key at start of Tables)
Filago pyramidata	broad-leaved cudweed	WCA8
Fumaria martinii	Martin's ramping-fumitory	WCA8
Gagea bohemica	early star- of-Bethlehem	WCA8
Galanthus nivalis	snowdrop	CITES2[a] ECH5 (if native)
Gentiana nivalis	alpine gentian	WCA8
Gentiana verna	spring gentian	WCA8
Gentianella anglica	early gentian	BC1 ECH2,4 WCA8
Gentianella ciliata	fringed gentian	WCA8
Gentianella uliginosa	dune gentian	WCA8
Gladiolus illyricus	wild gladiolus	WCA8
Gnaphalium luteoalbum	Jersey cudweed	WCA8
Goodyera repens	creeping lady's-tresses	CITES2
Gymnadenia conopsea	fragrant orchid	CITES2
Halimione pedunculata	stalked orache	WCA8
Hammarbya paludosa	bog orchid	CITES2
Herminium monorchis	musk orchid	CITES2
Hieracium attenuatifolium	weak-leaved hawkweed	WCA8
Hieracium northroense	North Roe hawkweed	WCA8
Hieracium zetlandicum	Shetland hawkweed	WCA8
Himantoglossum hircinum	lizard orchid	CITES2 WCA8
Homogyne alpina	purple colt's-foot	WCA8
Huperzia selago	fir clubmoss	ECH5
Hyacinthoides non-scripta	bluebell	WCA8(S13(2))
Lactuca saligna	least lettuce	WCA8
Leersia oryzoides	cut-grass	WCA8
Limosella australis	Welsh mudwort	WCA8
Liparis loeselii	fen orchid	BC1 CITES2 ECH2,4 WCA8
Listera cordata	lesser twayblade	CITES2
Listera ovata	twayblade	CITES2
Lloydia serotina	Snowdon lily	WCA8

[a] Except seeds, pollen/polinia, seedlings/tissue cultures produced *in vitro*, cut flowers from artificially propagated plants.

Species	Common English name	Protection (see key at start of Tables)
Luronium natans	floating water-plantain	BC1 ECH2,4 WCA8
Lychnis alpina	alpine catchfly	WCA8
Lycopodiella inundata	marsh clubmoss	ECH5
Lycopodium annotinum	interrupted clubmoss	ECH5
Lycopodium clavatum	stag's-horn clubmoss	ECH5
Lythrum hyssopifolia	grass-poly	WCA8
Melampyrum arvense	field cow-wheat	WCA8
Mentha pulegium	pennyroyal	WCA8
Minuartia stricta	Teesdale sandwort	WCA8
Najas flexilis	slender naiad	BC1 ECH2,4 WCA8
Najas marina	holly-leaved naiad	WCA8
Neotinea maculata	dense-flowered orchid	CITES2
Neottia nidus-avis	bird's-nest orchid	CITES2
Ononis reclinata	small restharrow	WCA8
Ophioglossum lusitanicum	least adder's-tongue	WCA8
Ophrys apifera	bee orchid	CITES2
Ophrys fuciflora	late spider-orchid	CITES2 WCA8
Ophrys insectifera	fly orchid	CITES2
Ophrys sphegodes	early spider-orchid	CITES2 WCA8
Orchis mascula	early-purple orchid	CITES2
Orchis militaris	military orchid	CITES2 WCA8
Orchis morio	green-winged orchid	CITES2
Orchis purpurea	lady orchid	CITES2
Orchis simia	monkey orchid	CITES2 WCA8
Orchis ustulata	burnt orchid	CITES2
Orobanche caryophyllacea	bedstraw broomrape	WCA8
Orobanche loricata	oxtongue broomrape	WCA8
Orobanche reticulata	thistle broomrape	WCA8
Petrorhagia nanteuilii	childing pink	WCA8
Phyllodoce caerulea	blue heath	WCA8
Phyteuma spicatum	spike rampion	WCA8
Platanthera bifolia	lesser butterfly-orchid	CITES2
Platanthera chlorantha	greater butterfly-orchid	CITES2

VERSION 02.2/CBEB 0501

Species	Common English name	Protection (see key at start of Tables)
Polygonatum verticillatum	whorled Solomon's-seal	WCA8
Polygonum maritimum	sea knotgrass	WCA8
Potentilla rupestris	rock cinquefoil	WCA8
Pulicaria vulgaris	small fleabane	WCA8
Pseudorchis albida	small-white orchid	CITES2
Pyrus cordata	Plymouth pear	WCA8
Ranunculus ophioglossifolius	adder's-tongue spearwort	WCA8
Rhinanthus serotinus	greater yellow-rattle	WCA8
Rhynchosinapis wrightii	Lundy cabbage	WCA8
Romulea columnae	sand crocus	WCA8
Rumex rupestris	shore dock	BC1 ECH2,4 WCA8
Ruscus aculeatus	butcher's broom	ECH5
Salvia pratensis	meadow clary	WCA8
Saxifraga cernua	drooping saxifrage	WCA8
Saxifraga cespitosa	tufted saxifrage	WCA8
Saxifraga hirculus	saxifrage, marsh	BC1 ECH2,4 WCA8
Scirpus triqueter	triangular club-rush	WCA8
Scleranthus perennis	perennial knawel	WCA8
Scorzonera humilis	viper's-grass	WCA8
Selinum carvifolia	Cambridge milk-parsley	WCA8
Senecio paludosus	fen ragwort	WCA8
Spiranthes aestivalis	summer lady's-tresses	BC1 CITES2 ECH2,4
Spiranthes romanzoffiana	Irish lady's-tresses	CITES2
Spiranthes spiralis	autumn lady's-tresses	CITES2
Stachys alpina	limestone woundwort	WCA8
Stachys germanica	downy woundwort	WCA8
Tephroseris integrifolia ssp. *maritima*	South Stack fleawort	WCA8
Teucrium botrys	cut-leaved germander	WCA8
Teucrium scordium	water germander	WCA8
Thlaspi perfoliatum	perfoliate penny-cress	WCA8
Trichomanes speciosum	Killarney fern	BC1 ECH2,4 WCA8
Veronica spicata	spiked speedwell	WCA8
Veronica triphyllos	fingered speedwell	WCA8

Species	Common English name	Protection (see key at start of Tables)
Viola persicifolia	fen violet	WCA8
Woodsia alpina	alpine woodsia	WCA8
Woodsia ilvensis	oblong woodsia	WCA8

Damasonium alisma Mill.
starfruit

PART B: PROTECTED SPECIES LISTED ALPHABETICALLY BY ENGLISH NAME

TABLE 1B: INVERTEBRATES IN ALPHABETICAL ORDER OF COMMON ENGLISH NAMES

Common English name	Species	Protection (see key at start of Tables)
apus	*Triops cancriformis*	WCA5
beetle, longhorn	*Cerambyx cerdo*	BC2 ECH2,4
beetle, mire pill	*Curimopsis nigrita*	WCA5(S9(4a))
beetle, Moccas	*Hypebaeus flavipes*	WCA5
beetle, rainbow leaf	*Chrysolina cerealis*	WCA5
beetle, stag	*Lucanus cervus*	BC3 ECH2 WCA5(S9(5))
beetle, violet click	*Limoniscus violaceus*	ECH2 WCA5
butterfly, Adonis blue	*Lysandra bellargus*	WCA5(S9(5))
butterfly, Apollo	*Parnassius apollo*	CITES2 ECH4
butterfly, black hairstreak	*Strymonidia pruni*	WCA5(S9(5))
butterfly, brown hairstreak	*Thecla betulae*	WCA5(S9(5))
butterfly, chalkhill blue	*Lysandra coridon*	WCA5(S9(5))
butterfly, checkered skipper	*Carterocephalus palaemon*	WCA5(S9(5))
butterfly, Duke of Burgundy fritillary	*Hamearis lucina*	WCA5(S9(5))
butterfly, Glanville fritillary	*Melitaea cinxia*	WCA5(S9(5))
butterfly, heath fritillary	*Melicta athalia*	WCA5
butterfly, high brown fritillary	*Argynnis adippe*	WCA5
butterfly, large heath	*Coenonympha tullia*	WCA5(S9(5))
butterfly, large blue	*Maculinea arion*	BC2 ECH4 WCA5
butterfly, large copper	*Lycaena dispar*	BC2 ECH2,4 WCA5
butterfly, large tortoiseshell	*Nymphalis polychloros*	WCA5(S9(5))
butterfly, Lulworth skipper	*Thymelicus acteon*	WCA5(S9(5))
butterfly, marsh fritillary	*Eurodryas aurinia*	WCA5
butterfly, mountain ringlet	*Erebia epiphron*	WCA5(S9(5))
butterfly, northern brown argus	*Aricia artaxerxes*	WCA5(S9(5))
butterfly, pearl-bordered fritillary	*Boloria euphrosyne*	WCA5(S9(5))
butterfly, purple emperor	*Apatura iris*	WCA5(S9(5))
butterfly, silver-spotted skipper	*Hesperia comma*	WCA5(S9(5))
butterfly, silver-studded blue	*Plebejus argus*	WCA5(S9(5))

Common English name	Species	Protection (see key at start of Tables)
butterfly, small blue	*Cupido minimus*	WCA5(S9(5))
butterfly, swallowtail	*Papilio machaon*	WCA5
butterfly, white-letter hairstreak	*Strymonidia w-album*	WCA5(S9(5))
butterfly, wood white	*Leptidea sinapis*	WCA5(S9(5))
cicada, New Forest	*Cicadetta montana*	WCA5
crayfish, Atlantic stream	*Austropotamobius pallipes*	BC3 ECH2 WCA5(S9(1) taking only, S9(5))
crayfish, noble	*Astacus astacus*	BC3 ECH5 (see Table 8)
cricket, field	*Gryllus campestris*	WCA5
cricket, mole	*Gryllotalpa gryllotalpa*	WCA5
damselfly, southern	*Coenagrion mercuriale*	BC2 ECH2 WCA5
dragonfly, Norfolk aeshna	*Aeshna isosceles*	WCA5
dragonfly, orange-spotted emerald	*Oxygastra curtesii*	BC2 ECH2,4
grasshopper, wart-biter	*Decticus verrucivorus*	WCA5
hatchet-snail, northern	*Thyasira gouldi*	WCA5
hydroid, marine	*Clavopsella navis*	WCA5
leech, medicinal	*Hirudo medicinalis*	BC3 CITES2 ECH5 WCA5
moth, barberry carpet	*Pareurlype berberata*	WCA5
moth, black-veined	*Siona lineata*	WCA5
moth, Curzon's sphinx	*Proserpinus proserpina*	BC2 ECH4
moth, Essex emerald	*Thetida smaragdaria maritima*	WCA5
moth, fiery clearwing	*Bembecia chrysidiformis*	WCA5
moth, Fisher's estuarine	*Gortyna borelii*	WCA5
moth, Jersey tiger	*Euplagia quadripunctaria*	ECH2
moth, New Forest burnet	*Zygaena viciae argyllensis*	WCA5
moth, reddish buff	*Acosmetia caliginosa*	WCA5
moth, Sussex emerald	*Thalera fimbrialis*	WCA5
mussel, fan	*Atrina fragilis*	WCA5(S9(1), S9(2), S9(5))
mussel, freshwater pearl	*Margaritifera margaritifera*	BC3 ECH2,5 WCA5
sandworm, lagoon	*Armandia cirrhosa*	WCA5
sea-anemone, Ivell's	*Edwardsia ivelli*	WCA5
sea-anemone, starlet	*Nematostella vectensis*	WCA5

Common English name	Species	Protection (see key at start of Tables)
sea-fan, pink	*Eunicella verrucosa*	WCA5(S9(1), S9(2), S9(5))
sea-mat, trembling	*Victorella pavida*	WCA5
sea-slug, lagoon	*Tenellia adspersa*	WCA5
shrimp, fairy	*Chirocephalus diaphanus*	WCA5
shrimp, lagoon sand	*Gammarus insensibilis*	WCA5
snail, De Folin's lagoon	*Caecum armoricum*	WCA5
snail, Desmoulins' whorl	*Vertigo moulinsiana*	ECH2
snail, glutinous	*Myxas glutinosa*	WCA5
snail, lagoon	*Paludinella littorina*	WCA5
snail, land	*Vertigo angustior*	ECH2
snail, land	*Vertigo genesii*	ECH2
snail, land	*Vertigo geyeri*	ECH2
snail, Roman	*Helix pomatia*	BC2 ECH2,4
snail, sandbowl	*Catinella arenaria*	WCA5
spider, fen raft	*Dolomedes plantarius*	WCA5
spider, ladybird	*Eresus niger*	WCA5
water- beetle	*Graphoderus bilineatus*	BC2 ECH2,4
water- beetle	*Graphoderus zonatus*	WCA5
water- beetle	*Paracymus aeneus*	WCA5
water-beetle, lesser silver	*Hydrochara caraboides*	WCA5
worm, tentacled lagoon	*Alkmaria romijni*	WCA5

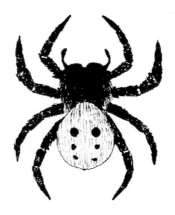

Eresus niger (Petagna)
ladybird spider

TABLE 2B: FISH IN ALPHABETICAL ORDER OF COMMON ENGLISH NAMES

Note there are various rules regarding fisheries and restrictions on season, methods, catches, *etc.* which are beyond the intended scope of the Checklist.

Common English name	Species	Protection (see key at start of Tables)
barbel	*Barbus barbus*	ECH5
bitterling	*Rhodeus sericeus*	BC3 ECH2 (see Table 8)
bullhead	*Cottus gobio*	ECH2
burbot	*Lota lota*	WCA5
goby, common	*Pomatoschistus microps*	BC3
goby, Couch's	*Gobius couchii*	WCA5
goby, giant	*Gobius cobitis*	WCA5
goby, sand	*Pomatoschistus minutus*	BC3
grayling	*Thymallus thymallus*	BC3 ECH5
houting	*Coregonus oxyrinchus*	BC3 ECH[a]2,4
lamprey, brook	*Lampetra planeri*	BC3 ECH2
lamprey, river	*Lampetra fluviatilis*	BC3 ECH2,5
lamprey, sea	*Petromyzon marinus*	BC3 ECH2
loach, spined	*Cobitis taenia*	BC3 ECH2
powan	*Coregonus lavaretus*	BC3 ECH5 WCA5
salmon, Atlantic	*Salmo salar*	BC3 ECH2,5 (only in fresh water)
shad, allis	*Alosa alosa*	BC3 ECH2,5 WCA5(S9(1), S9(4a))
shad, twaite	*Alosa fallax*	BC3 ECH2,5 WCA5(S9(4a))
shark, basking	*Cetorhinus maximus*	WC5 (see note in key)
sturgeon	*Acipenser sturio*	BC2 CITES1 ECH2,4 WCA5
vendace	*Coregonus albula*	BC3 ECH5 WCA5
wels	*Siluris glanis*	BC3 (see Table 8)

Lota lota (L.)
burbot

---

[a] Only anadromous populations in certain sectors of the North Sea covered by ECH

TABLE 3B: AMPHIBIANS AND REPTILES IN ALPHABETICAL ORDER OF COMMON ENGLISH NAMES

Common English name	Species	Protection (see key at start of Tables)
adder	*Vipera berus*	BC3 WCA5(S9(1) killing/injuring only, S9(5))
frog, common	*Rana temporaria*	BC3 WCA5(S9(5))
frog, edible	*Rana esculenta*	BC3 ECH5
frog, European tree	*Hyla arborea*	BC2 ECH4 (see Table 8)
frog, marsh	*Rana ridibunda*	BC3 ECH5 (see Table 8)
frog, pool	*Rana lessonae*	BC3 ECH4
lizard, common	*Lacerta vivipara*	BC3 WCA5(S9(1) killing/injuring only, S9(5))
lizard, common wall	*Podarcis muralis*	BC2 ECH4
lizard, sand	*Lacerta agilis*	BC2 ECH4 WCA5
newt, alpine	*Triturus alpestris*	BC3 (see Table 8)
newt, great crested	*Triturus cristatus cristatus*	BC2 ECH2,4 WCA5
newt, Italian crested	*Triturus cristatus carnifex*	BC2 ECH2,4 (see Table 8)
newt, palmate	*Triturus helveticus*	BC3 WCA5(S9(5))
newt, smooth	*Triturus vulgaris*	BC3 WCA5(S9(5))
slow-worm	*Anguis fragilis*	BC3 WCA5(S9(1) killing/injuring only, S9(5))
snake, Aesculapian	*Elaphe longissima*	BC2 ECH4 (see Table 8)
snake, grass	*Natrix natrix*	BC3 WCA5(S9(1) killing/injuring only, S9(5))
snake, smooth	*Coronella austriaca*	BC2 ECH4 WCA5
terrapin, European pond	*Emys orbicularis*	BC2 ECH2,4 (see Table 8)
toad, common	*Bufo bufo*	BC3 WCA5(S9(5))
toad, midwife	*Alytes obstetricans*	BC2 ECH4 (see Table 8)
toad, natterjack	*Bufo calamita*	BC2 ECH4 WCA5
toad, yellow-bellied	*Bombina variegata*	BC2 ECH2,4 (see Table 8)
turtle, green	*Chelonia mydas*	BC2 BoC1,2 CITES1 ECH4 WCA5
turtle, hawk's-bill	*Eretmochelys imbricata*	BC2 BoC1,2 CITES1 ECH4 WCA5
turtle, Kemp's ridley	*Lepidochelys kempii*	BC2 BoC1,2 CITES1 ECH4 WCA5
turtle, leatherback	*Dermochelys coriacea*	BC2 BoC1,2 CITES1 ECH4 WCA5
turtle, loggerhead	*Caretta caretta*	BC2 BoC1,2 CITES1 ECH2,4 WCA5

TABLE 4B: BIRDS IN ALPHABETICAL ORDER OF COMMON ENGLISH NAMES

With the exception of 13 very abundant or pest species (great and lesser black-backed gull, herring gull, wood pigeon, house sparrow, starling, jay, magpie, carrion crow, rook, jackdaw, feral pigeon and collared dove) which may be killed by authorized persons, the Wildlife and Countryside Act gives general protection to **all** wild birds in Britain from killing, injuring or taking as well as taking, damaging or destroying nests in use or being built, and taking or destroying eggs. Only birds which have special protection under the Wildlife and Countryside Act are listed in this Table. Appendix III of the Berne Convention includes all birds not listed in Appendix II except 11 abundant/pest species (great and lesser black-backed gull, herring gull, wood pigeon, house sparrow, starling, jay, magpie, carrion crow, rook, jackdaw). Berne Convention Appendix III has therefore been ignored for the purposes of this Checklist but readers should nonetheless take note of its existence. With regard to the EC Birds Directive, only species on the Directive's specially protected Annex I list are included in the Checklist. Birds only required to be registered and ringed if kept in captivity (WCA Schedule 4) are also excluded as are game birds (which have particular rules) not enjoying **special** protection in the close season. Birds on Bonn Convention Appendix II only appear in this Checklist if they are listed under other instruments. Please also note the Bonn Convention Agreement protecting African-Eurasian migratory waterbirds which includes, *inter alia*, all the **Anatidae**.

Many species of birds are only occasional visitors to Britain and it has been difficult to decide which of these to include. Please therefore note that some protected species which are recorded only very rarely as vagrants to Britain are excluded from this Checklist.

Common English name	Species	Protection (see key at start of Tables)
avocet	*Recurvirostra avocetta*	BC2 BoC2 ECB WCA1i
bee-eater	*Merops apiaster*	BC2 BoC2 WCA1i
bittern	*Botaurus stellaris*	BC2 BoC2 ECB WCA1i
bittern, little	*Ixobrychus minutus*	BC2 BoC2 ECB WCA1i
blackcap	*Sylvia atricapilla*	BC2
bluethroat	*Luscinia svecica*	BC2 ECB WCA1i
brambling	*Fringilla montifringilla*	WCA1i
bunting, cirl	*Emberiza cirlus*	BC2 WCA1i
bunting, Lapland	*Calcarius lapponicus*	BC2 WCA1i
bunting, reed	*Emberiza schoeniclus*	BC2
bunting, snow	*Plectrophenax nivalis*	BC2 WCA1i
buzzard	*Buteo buteo*	BC2 BoC2
buzzard, honey	*Pernis apivorus*	BC2 BoC2 ECB WCA1i
buzzard, rough-legged	*Buteo lagopus*	BC2 BoC2
capercaillie	*Tetrao urogallus*	ECB (exceptions outside close season; voluntary ban on shooting)
chiffchaff	*Phylloscopus collybita*	BC2
chough	*Pyrrhocorax pyrrhocorax*	BC2 ECB WCA1i
corncrake	*Crex crex*	BC2 ECB WCA1i
courser, cream-coloured	*Cursorius cursor*	BC2 ECB
crake, spotted	*Porzana porzana*	BC2 BoC2 ECB WCA1i
crane, common	*Grus grus*	BC2 BoC2 CITES2 ECB

Common English name	Species	Protection (see key at start of Tables)
crossbill	*Loxia curvirostra*	BC2 WCA1i
crossbill, parrot	*Loxia pytyopsittacus*	BC2 WCA1i
crossbill, Scottish	*Loxia scotica*	BC2 ECB WCA1i
crossbill, two-barred	*Loxia leucoptera*	BC2 WCA1i
curlew, stone	*Burhinus oedicnemus*	BC2 BoC2 ECB WCA1i
dipper	*Cinclus cinclus*	BC2
diver, black-throated	*Gavia arctica*	BC2 BoC2 ECB WCA1i
diver, great northern	*Gavia immer*	BC2 BoC2 ECB WCA1i
diver, red-throated	*Gavia stellata*	BC2 BoC2 ECB WCA1i
diver, white-billed	*Gavia adamsii*	BC2 BoC2 WCA1i
dotterel	*Charadrius morinellus*	BC2 BoC2 ECB WCA1i
duck, harlequin	*Histrionicus histrionicus*	BC2 BoC2
duck, long-tailed	*Clangula hyemalis*	BoC2 WCA1i
dunlin	*Calidris alpina*	BC2 BoC2
dunnock	*Prunella modularis*	BC2
eagle, golden	*Aquila chrysaetos*	BC2 BoC2 ECB WCA1i
eagle, white-tailed	*Haliaeetus albicilla*	BC2 BoC1,2 CITES1 ECB WCA1i
egret, cattle	*Bubulcus ibis*	BC2 CITES3
egret, great white	*Egretta alba*	BC2 CITES3 ECB
egret, little	*Egretta garzetta*	BC2 CITES3 ECB
fieldfare	*Turdus pilaris*	WCA1i
firecrest	*Regulus ignicapillus*	BC2 WCA1i
flycatcher, pied	*Ficedula hypoleuca*	BC2 BoC2
flycatcher, spotted	*Muscicapa striata*	BC2 BoC2
garganey	*Anas querquedula*	BoC2 CITES3 WCA1i
godwit, black-tailed	*Limosa limosa*	BoC2 WCA1i
goldcrest	*Regulus regulus*	BC2
goldeneye	*Bucephala clangula*	BoC2 ECB WCA1ii
goldfinch	*Carduelis carduelis*	BC2
goose, barnacle	*Branta leucopsis*	BoC2 BC2 ECB
goose, greylag	*Anser anser*	BoC2 WCA1ii (restricted areas)
goose, red-breasted	*Branta ruficollis*	BC2 BoC2 CITES2 ECB

Common English name	Species	Protection (see key at start of Tables)
goose, white-fronted (Greenland race)	*Anser albifrons flavirostris*	BoC2 ECB
goshawk	*Accipiter gentilis*	BC2 BoC2 WCA1i
grebe, black-necked	*Podiceps nigricollis*	BC2 WCA1i
grebe, little	*Podiceps ruficollis*	BC2
grebe, red-necked	*Podiceps grisegena*	BC2 BoC2
grebe, Slavonian	*Podiceps auritus*	BC2 BoC2 ECB WCA1i
greenfinch	*Carduelis chloris*	BC2
greenshank	*Tringa nebularia*	BoC2 WCA1i
gull, little	*Larus minutus*	BC2 WCA1i
gull, Mediterranean	*Larus melanocephalus*	BC2 ECB WCA1i
gull, Sabine's	*Larus sabini*	BC2
gull, slender-billed	*Larus genei*	BC2 ECB
gyrfalcon	*Falco rusticolus*	BC2 BoC2 CITES1 ECB WCA1i
harrier, hen	*Circus cyaneus*	BC2 BoC2 ECB WCA1i
harrier, marsh	*Circus aeruginosus*	BC2 BoC2 ECB WCA1i
harrier, Montagu's	*Circus pygargus*	BC2 BoC2 ECB WCA1i
hawfinch	*Coccothraustes coccothraustes*	BC2
heron, night	*Nycticorax nycticorax*	BC2 ECB
heron, purple	*Ardea purpurea*	BC2 BoC2 (if breeding) ECB WCA1i
heron, squacco	*Ardeola ralloides*	BC2 ECB
hobby	*Falco subbuteo*	BC2 BoC2 CITES2 WCA1i
hoopoe	*Upupa epops*	BC2 WCA1i
ibis, glossy	*Plegadis falcinellus*	BC2 BoC2 ECB
kestrel	*Falco tinnunculus*	BC2 BoC2 CITES2
kingfisher	*Alcedo atthis*	BC2 ECB WCA1i
kite, black	*Milvus migrans*	BC2 BoC2 ECB
kite, red	*Milvus milvus*	BC2 BoC2 ECB WCA1i
lark, shore	*Eremophila alpestris*	BC2 WCA1i
lark, wood	*Lullula arborea*	ECB WCA1i
linnet	*Carduelis cannabina*	BC2
martin, house	*Delichon urbica*	BC2
martin, sand	*Hirundo riparia*	BC2

Common English name	Species	Protection (see key at start of Tables)
merlin	*Falco columbarius*	BC2 BoC2 CITES2 ECB WCA1i
nightingale	*Luscinia megarhynchos*	BC2
nightjar	*Caprimulgus europaeus*	BC2 ECB
nightjar, Egyptian	*Caprimulgus aegyptius*	BC2
nightjar, red-necked	*Caprimulgus ruficollis*	BC2
nuthatch	*Sitta europaea*	BC2
oriole, golden	*Oriolus oriolus*	BC2 WCA1i
osprey	*Pandion haliaetus*	BC2 BoC2 ECB WCA1i
owl, barn	*Tyto alba*	BC2 WCA1i
owl, little	*Athene noctua*	BC2 CITES2
owl, long-eared	*Asio otus*	BC2 CITES2
owl, short-eared	*Asio flammeus*	BC2 CITES2 ECB
owl, snowy	*Nyctea scandiaca*	BC2 ECB CITES2 WCA1i
owl, tawny	*Strix aluco*	BC2 CITES2
peregrine	*Falco peregrinus*	BC2 BoC2 CITES1 ECB WCA1i
petrel, Leach's	*Oceanodroma leucorhoa*	BC2 ECB WCA1i
petrel, storm	*Hydrobates pelagicus*	BC2 ECB
phalarope, grey	*Phalaropus fulicarius*	BC2 BoC2
phalarope, red-necked	*Phalaropus lobatus*	BC2 BoC2 ECB WCA1i
phalarope, Wilson's	*Phalaropus tricolor*	BC2 BoC2
pintail	*Anas acuta*	BoC2 CITES3 WCA1ii
pipit, meadow	*Anthus pratensis*	BC2
pipit, rock	*Anthus petrosus*	BC2
pipit, tree	*Anthus trivialis*	BC2
pipit, water	*Anthus spinoletta*	BC2
plover, golden	*Pluvialis apricaria*	BoC2 ECB (exceptions outside close season)
plover, Kentish	*Charadrius alexandrinus*	BC2 BoC2 WCA1i
plover, little ringed	*Charadrius dubius*	BC2 BoC2 WCA1i
plover, ringed	*Charadrius hiaticula*	BC2 BoC2
pratincole, collared	*Glareola pratincola*	BC2 BoC2 ECB
quail, common	*Coturnix coturnix*	BoC2 WCA1i
redpoll	*Carduelis flammea*	BC2

Common English name	Species	Protection (see key at start of Tables)
redstart	*Phoenicurus phoenicurus*	BC2
redstart, black	*Phoenicurus ochruros*	BC2 WCA1i
redwing	*Turdus iliacus*	WCA1i
reedling, bearded	*Panurus biarmicus*	BC2 WCA1i
robin	*Erithacus rubecula*	BC2
roller	*Coracias garrulus*	BC2 BoC2 ECB
rosefinch, scarlet	*Carpodacus erythrinus*	BC2 WCA1i
ruff	*Philomachus pugnax*	BoC2 ECB WCA1i
sanderling	*Calidris alba*	BC2 BoC2
sandgrouse, Pallas'	*Syrrhaptes paradoxus*	BC2
sandpiper, common	*Tringa hypoleucos*	BC2 BoC2
sandpiper, curlew	*Calidris ferruginea*	BC2 BoC2
sandpiper, green	*Tringa ochropus*	BC2 BoC2 WCA1i
sandpiper, purple	*Calidris maritima*	BC2 BoC2 WCA1i
sandpiper, wood	*Tringa glareola*	BC2 BoC2 ECB WCA1i
scaup	*Aythya marila*	BoC2 WCA1i
scoter, common	*Melanitta nigra*	BoC2 WCA1i
scoter, velvet	*Melanitta fusca*	BoC2 WCA1i
serin	*Serinus serinus*	BC2 WCA1i
shearwater, Manx	*Puffinus puffinus*	BC2
shelduck, common	*Tadorna tadorna*	BC2 BoC2
shelduck, ruddy	*Tadorna ferruginea*	BC2 BoC2 ECB
shrike, great grey	*Lanius excubitor*	BC2
shrike, red-backed	*Lanius collurio*	BC2 ECB WCA1i
siskin	*Carduelis spinus*	BC2
smew	*Mergus albellus*	BC2 BoC2
snipe, great	*Gallinago media*	BC2 BoC2 ECB
sparrowhawk	*Accipiter nisus*	BC2 BoC2
spoonbill	*Platalea leucorodia*	BC2 BoC2 CITES2 ECB WCA1i
stilt, black-winged	*Himantopus himantopus*	BC2 BoC2 ECB WCA1i
stint, little	*Calidris minuta*	BC2 BoC2
stint, Teminck's	*Calidris temminckii*	BC2 BoC2 WCA1i

Common English name	Species	Protection (see key at start of Tables)
stonechat	*Saxicola torquata*	BC2
stork, black	*Ciconia nigra*	BC2 BoC2 CITES2 ECB
stork, white	*Ciconia ciconia*	BC2 BoC2 ECB
swallow	*Hirundo rustica*	BC2
swan, Bewick's	*Cygnus columbianus bewickii*	BoC2 BC2 ECB WCA1i
swan, whooper	*Cygnus cygnus*	BC2 BoC2 ECB WCA1i
swift, alpine	*Apus melba*	BC2
swift, pallid	*Apus pallida*	BC2
teal, Baikal	*Anas formosa*	BoC2 CITES2
tern, arctic	*Sterna paradisaea*	BC2 BoC2 ECB
tern, black	*Chlidonias niger*	BC2 BoC2 ECB WCA1i
tern, Caspian	*Sterna caspia*	BC2 BoC2 ECB
tern, common	*Sterna hirundo*	BC2 BoC2 ECB
tern, gull-billed	*Gelochelidon nilotica*	BC2 ECB
tern, little	*Sterna albifrons*	BC2 BoC2 ECB WCA1i
tern, roseate	*Sterna dougallii*	BC2 BoC2 ECB WCA1i
tern, Sandwich	*Sterna sandvicensis*	BC2 BoC2 ECB
tern, whiskered	*Chlidonias hybridus*	BC2 ECB
tit, blue	*Parus caeruleus*	BC2
tit, coal	*Parus ater*	BC2
tit, crested	*Parus cristatus*	BC2 WCA1i
tit, great	*Parus major*	BC2
tit, long-tailed	*Aegithalos caudatus*	BC2
tit, marsh	*Parus palustris*	BC2
tit, willow	*Parus montanus*	BC2
treecreeper	*Certhia familiaris*	BC2
treecreeper, short-toed	*Certhia brachydactyla*	BC2 WCA1i
turnstone	*Arenaria interpres*	BC2 BoC2
twite	*Carduelis flavirostris*	BC2
wagtail, grey	*Motacilla cinerea*	BC2
wagtail, pied	*Motacilla alba*	BC2
wagtail, yellow	*Motacilla flava*	BC2

Common English name	Species	Protection (see key at start of Tables)
warbler, Cetti's	*Cettia cetti*	BC2 WCA1i
warbler, Dartford	*Sylvia undata*	BC2 ECB WCA1i
warbler, fan-tailed	*Cisticola juncidis*	BC2
warbler, garden	*Sylvia borin*	BC2
warbler, grasshopper	*Locustella naevia*	BC2
warbler, marsh	*Acrocephalus palustris*	BC2 WCA1i
warbler, reed	*Acrocephalus scirpaceus*	BC2
warbler, Savi's	*Locustella luscinioides*	BC2 WCA1i
warbler, sedge	*Acrocephalus schoenobaenus*	BC2
warbler, willow	*Phylloscopus trochilus*	BC2
warbler, wood	*Phylloscopus sibilatrix*	BC2
waxwing	*Bombycilla garrulus*	BC2
wheatear	*Oenanthc ocnanthe*	BC2
whimbrel	*Numenius phaeopus*	BoC2 WCA1i
whinchat	*Saxicola rubetra*	BC2
whitethroat, common	*Sylvia communis*	BC2
whitethroat, lesser	*Sylvia curruca*	BC2
woodpecker, great spotted	*Dendrocopos major*	BC2
woodpecker, green	*Picus viridis*	BC2
woodpecker, lesser spotted	*Dendrocopos minor*	BC2
wren	*Troglodytes troglodytes*	BC2
wryneck	*Jynx torquilla*	BC2 WCA1i
yellowhammer	*Emberiza citrinella*	BC2

Nycticorax nycticorax
night heron

TABLE 5B: MAMMALS IN ALPHABETICAL ORDER OF COMMON ENGLISH NAMES

Only limited conservation protection is afforded to some mammals below (but see Note at end of this Table regarding cruelty). Note that ALL cetaceans (whales and dolphins) are protected from any intentional or reckless disturbance.

Common English name	Species	Protection (see key at start of Tables)
badger	*Meles meles*	BC3 PBA WCA6
barbastelle	*Barbastella barbastellus*	BC2 BoC2 ECH2,4 WCA5,6
bat, Bechstein's	*Myotis bechsteinii*	BC2 BoC2 ECH2,4 WCA5,6
bat, Brandt's	*Myotis brandtii*	BC2 BoC2 ECH4 WCA5,6
bat, brown long-eared	*Plecotus auritus*	BC2 BoC2 ECH4 WCA5,6
bat, Daubenton's	*Myotis daubentonii*	BC2 BoC2 ECH4 WCA5,6
bat, greater horseshoe	*Rhinolophus ferrumequinum*	BC2 BoC2 ECH2,4 WCA5,6
bat, grey long-eared	*Plecotus austriacus*	BC2 BoC2 ECH4 WCA5,6
bat, Leisler's	*Nyctalus leisleri*	BC2 BoC2 ECH4 WCA5,6
bat, lesser horseshoe	*Rhinolophus hipposideros*	BC2 BoC2 ECH2,4 WCA5,6
bat, mouse-eared	*Myotis myotis*	BC2 BoC2 ECH2,4 WCA5,6
bat, Natterer's	*Myotis nattereri*	BC2 BoC2 ECH4 WCA5,6
bat, whiskered	*Myotis mystacinus*	BC2 BoC2 ECH4 WCA5,6
cat, wild	*Felis silvestris*	BC2 ECH4 CITES2 WCA5,6
deer, fallow	*Dama dama*	BC3 DA DSA
deer, red	*Cervus elaphus*	BC3 DA DSA (see also Table 8)
deer, roe	*Capreolus capreolus*	BC3 DA DSA
deer, sika	*Cervus nippon*	BC3 DA DSA (see also Table 8)
deer, water	*Hydropotes inermis*	BC3 DA DSA
dolphin, Atlantic white-sided	*Lagenorhynchus acutus*	BC2 BoC2 CITES2 ECH4 WCA5
dolphin, bottle-nosed	*Tursiops truncatus*	BC2 BoC2 CITES2 ECH2,4 WCA5,6
dolphin, common	*Delphinus delphis*	BC2 BoC2 CITES2 ECH4 WCA5,6
dolphin, Risso's	*Grampus griseus*	BC2 BoC2 CITES2 ECH4 WCA5
dolphin, striped	*Stenella coeruleoalba*	BC2 (BoC2)[a] CITES2 ECH4 WCA5
dolphin, white-beaked	*Lagenorhynchus albirostris*	BC2 BoC2 CITES2 ECH4 WCA5
dormouse, common	*Muscardinus avellanarius*	BC3 ECH4 WCA5,6

[a] Occasional visitor to British waters - the Western Mediterranean population of *S.coeruleoalba* is on BoC2

Common English name	Species	Protection (see key at start of Tables)
dormouse, edible	*Glis glis*	BC3 WCA6
hare, mountain	*Lepus timidus*	BC3 ECH5
hedgehog	*Erinaceus europaeus*	BC3 WCA6
marten, pine	*Martes martes*	BC3 ECH5 WCA5,6
muntjac	*Muntiacus reevesii*	BC3 DA DSA[a]
narwhal	*Monodon monoceros*	BC2 BoC2 CITES2 ECH4 WCA5
noctule	*Nyctalus noctula*	BC2 BoC2 ECH4 WCA5,6
otter	*Lutra lutra*	BC2 ECH2,4 CITES1 WCA5,6
pipistrelle[b]	*Pipistrellus pipistrellus*	BC3 BoC2 ECH4 WCA5,6
polecat	*Mustela putorius*	BC3 ECH5 WCA6
porpoise, harbour	*Phocoena phocoena*	BC2 BoC2 CITES2 ECH2,4 WCA5,6
reindeer[c]	*Rangifer tarandus*	BC3 DA DSA
seal, bearded	*Erignathus barbatus*	BC3 CSA (partial) ECH5
seal, common	*Phoca vitulina*	BC3 CSA ECH2
seal, grey	*Halichoerus grypus*	BC3 CSA ECH2
seal, harp	*Phoca groenlandica*	BC3 CSA (partial) ECH5
seal, hooded	*Cystophora cristata*	BC3 CSA (partial) ECH5
serotine	*Eptesicus serotinus*	BC2 BoC2 ECH4 WCA5,6
shrew, common	*Sorex araneus*	BC3 WCA6
shrew, lesser white-toothed	*Crocidura suaveolens*	BC3 WCA6
shrew, pygmy	*Sorex minutus*	BC3 WCA6
shrew, water	*Neomys fodiens*	BC3 WCA6
squirrel, red	*Sciurus vulgaris*	BC3 WCA5,6
stoat	*Mustela erminea*	BC3
vole, water	*Arvicola terrestris*	WCA5(S9(4a, 4b))
walrus	*Odobenus rosmarus*	BC2 CITES3 WCA5
weasel	*Mustela nivalis*	BC3

[a] Unlikely to be found in Scotland, but spreading.

[b] Now believed to be two closely related spp.

[c] Extinct in wild but free-ranging managed herd in Cairngorms

Common English name	Species	Protection (see key at start of Tables)
whale, blue	*Balaenoptera musculus*	BC3 BoC1 CITES1 ECH4 WCA5
whale, Cuvier's beaked	*Ziphius cavirostris*	BC2 CITES2 ECH4 WCA5
whale, false killer	*Pseudorca crassidens*	BC2 CITES2 ECH4 WCA5
whale, fin	*Balaenoptera physalus*	BC3 CITES1 ECH4 WCA5
whale, Gervais' beaked	*Mesoplodon europaeus*	BC3 CITES2 ECH4 WCA5
whale, humpback	*Megaptera novaeangliae*	BC2 BoC1 CITES1 ECH4 WCA5
whale, killer	*Orcinus orca*	BC2 BoC2 CITES2 ECH4 WCA5
whale, long-finned pilot	*Globicephala melas*	BC2 BoC2 CITES2 ECH4 WCA5
whale, minke	*Balaenoptera acutorostrata*	BC3 CITES1 ECH4 WCA5
whale, northern bottlenose	*Hyperoodon ampullatus*	BC3 BoC2 CITES1 ECH4 WCA5
whale, northern right	*Eubalaena glacialis*	BC2 BoC1 CITES1 ECH4 WCA5
whale, pygmy sperm	*Kogia breviceps*	BC2 CITES1 ECH4 WCA5
whale, sei	*Balaenoptera borealis*	BC3 CITES1 ECH4 WCA5
whale, Sowerby's beaked	*Mesoplodon bidens*	BC2 CITES2 ECH4 WCA5
whale, sperm	*Physeter macrocephalus*	BC3 CITES1 ECH4 WCA5
whale, True's beaked	*Mesoplodon mirus*	BC2 CITES2 ECH4 WCA5
whale, white	*Delphinapterus leucas*	BC3 BoC2 CITES2 ECH4 WCA5

Note: The Wild Mammals (Protection) Act was passed in 1996. With certain exceptions such as lawful hunting, vermin trapping and humane destruction, this legislation makes it an offence to mutilate, kick, beat, impale, stab, burn, stone, crush, drown, drag or asphyxiate any wild mammal with intent to inflict unnecessary suffering.

Muscardinus avellanarius L.
common dormouse

VERSION 02.2/CBEB 0501

TABLE 6B: ALGAE, LICHENS, BRYOPHYTES, STONEWORTS (NON-VASCULAR PLANTS) AND FUNGI IN ALPHABETICAL ORDER OF COMMON ENGLISH NAMES

Protected species include any subspecies or varieties - these are not listed separately in the Table.

Common English name	Species	Protection (see key at start of Tables)
anomodon, long-leaved	*Anomodon longifolius*	WCA8
apple-moss, rigid	*Bartramia stricta*	WCA8
beard-moss, cordate	*Barbula cordata*	WCA8
beech-lichen, New Forest	*Enterographa elaborata*	WCA8
blackwort	*Southbya nigrella*	WCA8
bolete, royal	*Boletus regius*	WCA8
braer-moss, glaucous	*Barbula glauca*	WCA8
breck-lichen, scaly	*Squamarina lentigera*	WCA8
breck-lichen, starry	*Buellia asterella*	WCA8
bright green cave-moss,	*Cyclodictyon laetevirens*	WCA8
bristle-moss, blunt-leaved	*Orthotrichum obtusifolium*	WCA8
caloplaca, snow	*Caloplaca nivalis*	WCA8
catapyrenium, tree	*Catapyrenium psoromoides*	WCA8
catillaria, Laurer's	*Catillaria laureri*	WCA8
cladonia, convoluted	*Cladonia convoluta*	WCA8
cladonia, upright mountain	*Cladonia stricta*	WCA8
copper-moss, alpine	*Mielichhoferia mielichhoferi*	WCA8
crystalwort, Lizard	*Riccia bifurca*	WCA8
cushion, dryad's	*Leucobryum glaucum*	ECH5
dew-moss, blue	*Saelania glaucescens*	WCA8
dog-lichen, ear-lobed	*Peltigera lepidophora*	WCA8
earwort, marsh	*Jamesoniella undulifolia*	WCA8
elm-lichen, orange-fruited	*Caloplaca luteoalba*	WCA8
feather-moss, Derbyshire	*Thamnobryum angustifolium*	WCA8
feather-moss, large yellow	*Scorpidium turgescens*	WCA8
feather-moss, Polar	*Hygrohypnum polare*	WCA8
feather-moss, round-leaved	*Rhynchostegium rotundifolium*	WCA8
feather-moss, slender green	*Drepanocladus vernicosus*	BC1 ECH2 WCA8

Common English name	Species	Protection (see key at start of Tables)
feather-moss, Vaucher's	*Hypnum vaucheri*	WCA8
flapwort, Norfolk	*Leiocolea rutheana*	WCA8
frostwort, pointed	*Gymnomitrion apiculatum*	WCA8
fungus, hedgehog	*Hericium erinaceum*	WCA8
goblin-lights	*Catolechia wahlenbergii*	WCA8
grimmia, blunt-leaved	*Grimmia unicolor*	WCA8
gyalecta, elm	*Gyalecta ulmi*	WCA8
hair-lichen, forked	*Bryoria furcellata*	WCA8
hair-lichen, golden	*Teloschistes flavicans*	WCA8
kidney-lichen, arctic	*Nephroma arcticum*	WCA8
lecanactis, churchyard	*Lecanactis hemisphaerica*	WCA8
lecanora, tarn	*Lecanora achariana*	WCA8
lecidea, copper	*Lecidea inops*	WCA8
lichen, reindeer	*Cladonia arbuscula* (subgen. *Cladina*)	ECH5
lichen, reindeer	*Cladonia ciliata* (subgen. *Cladina*)	ECH5
lichen, reindeer	*Cladonia mediterranea* (subgen. *Cladina*)	ECH5
lichen, reindeer	*Cladonia mitis* (subgen. *Cladina*)	ECH5
lichen, reindeer	*Cladonia portentosa* (subgen. *Cladina*)	ECH5
lichen, reindeer	*Cladonia rangiferina* (subgen. *Cladina*)	ECH5
lichen, reindeer	*Cladonia stellaris* (subgen. *Cladina*)	ECH5
lichen, reindeer	*Cladonia stygia* (subgen. *Cladina*)	ECH5
lichen, river jelly	*Collema dichotomum*	WCA8
liverwort, Lindenberg's leafy	*Adelanthus lindenbergianus*	WCA8
maerl	*Phymatolithon calcareum*	ECH5
maerl	*Lithothamnium corallioides*	ECH5
millimetre moss,	*Micromitrium tenerum*	WCA8
moss, Austin's bog	*Sphagnum imbricatum*	ECH5
moss, Baltic bog	*Sphagnum balticum*	ECH5 WCA8
moss, blunt-leaved bog	*Sphagnum palustre*	ECH5
moss, blushing bog	*Sphagnum molle*	ECH5
moss, cleft bog	*Sphagnum riparium*	ECH5
moss, compact bog	*Sphagnum compactum*	ECH5

Common English name	Species	Protection (see key at start of Tables)
moss, cow-horn bog	*Sphagnum auriculatum*	ECH5
moss, feathery bog	*Sphagnum cuspidatum*	ECH5
moss, five-ranked bog	*Sphagnum quinquefarium*	ECH5
moss, flamingo	*Desmatodon cernuus*	WCA8
moss, flat-leaved bog	*Sphagnum platyphyllum*	ECH5
moss, flexuous bog	*Sphagnum recurvum*	ECH5
moss, fringed bog	*Sphagnum fimbriatum*	ECH5
moss, Girgensohn's bog	*Sphagnum girgensohnii*	ECH5
moss, golden bog	*Sphagnum pulchrum*	ECH5
moss, knothole	*Zygodon forsteri*	WCA8
moss, Lindberg's bog	*Sphagnum lindbergii*	ECH5
moss, lustrous bog	*Sphagnum subnitens*	ECH5
moss, Magellanic bog	*Sphagnum magellanicum*	ECH5
moss, Nowell's limestone	*Zygodon gracilis*	WCA8
moss, obtuse bog	*Sphagnum obtusum*	ECH5
moss, olive bog	*Sphagnum majus*	ECH5
moss, pale bog	*Sphagnum strictum*	ECH5
moss, papillose bog	*Sphagnum papillosum*	ECH5
moss, red bog	*Sphagnum capillifolium*	ECH5
moss, rigid bog	*Sphagnum teres*	ECH5
moss, Russow's bog	*Sphagnum russowii*	ECH5
moss, rusty bog	*Sphagnum fuscum*	ECH5
moss, slender cow-horn bog	*Sphagnum subsecundum*	ECH5
moss, soft bog	*Sphagnum tenellum*	ECH5
moss, spiky bog	*Sphagnum squarrosum*	ECH5
moss, twisted bog	*Sphagnum contortum*	ECH5
moss, Warnstorf's bog	*Sphagnum warnstorfii*	ECH5
pannaria, Caledonia	*Pannaria ignobilis*	WCA8
parmelia, New Forest	*Parmelia minarum*	WCA8
parmentaria, oil stain	*Parmentaria chilensis*	WCA8
path-moss, Cornish	*Ditrichum cornubicum*	WCA8
pertusaria, alpine moss	*Pertusaria bryontha*	WCA8

Common English name	Species	Protection (see key at start of Tables)
petalwort	*Petalophyllum ralfsii*	BC1 ECH2 WCA8
physcia, southern grey	*Physcia tribacioides*	WCA8
polypore, oak	*Buglossoporus pulvinus*	WCA8
pseudocyphellaria, ragged	*Pseudocyphellaria lacerata*	WCA8
psora, rusty alpine	*Psora rubiformis*	WCA8
puffball, sandy stilt	*Battarraea phalloides*	WCA8
pygmy-moss, triangular	*Acaulon triquetrum*	WCA8
river-moss, multi-fruited	*Cryphaea lamyana*	WCA8
rosette-lichen, coralloid	*Heterodermia propagulifera*	WCA8
rustwort, western	*Marsupella profunda*	BC1 ECH2 WCA8
shield-moss, green	*Buxbaumia viridis*	BC1 ECH2 WCA8
silk-moss, hair	*Plagiothecium piliferum*	WCA8
solenopsora, serpentine	*Solenopsora liparina*	WCA8
stonewort, bearded	*Chara canescens*	WCA8
stonewort, foxtail	*Lamprothamnium papulosum*	WCA8 (BC proposed 1992)
strap-lichen, ciliate	*Heterodermia leucomelos*	WCA8
sulphur-tresses, alpine	*Alectoria ochroleuca*	WCA8
thread-moss , long-leaved	*Bryum neodamense*	WCA8
thread-moss, dune	*Bryum mamillatum*	WCA8
thread-moss, Schleicher's	*Bryum schleicheri* var. *latifolium*	WCA8
turpswort	*Geocalyx graveolens*	WCA8

Leucobryum glaucum (Hedw.) Ångstr.
dryad's cushion

VERSION 02.2/CBEB 0501

TABLE 7B: TRACHEOPHYTES (VASCULAR PLANTS) IN ALPHABETICAL ORDER OF COMMON ENGLISH NAMES

Protected species include any subspecies or varieties and, in the **Orchidaceae** (orchids) interspecific and intergeneric hybrids - these are not listed separately in the Table. Parts and derivatives are also included.

Common English name	Species	Protection (see key at start of Tables)
adder's-tongue, least	Ophioglossum lusitanicum	WCA8
alison, small	Alyssum alyssoides	WCA8
blue-sow-thistle, alpine	Cicerbita alpina	WCA8
bluebell	Hyacinthoides non-scripta	WCA8(S13(2))
brome, interrupted	Bromus interruptus	BC1
broom, butcher's	Ruscus aculeatus	ECH5
broomrape, bedstraw	Orobanche caryophyllacea	WCA8
broomrape, oxtongue	Orobanche loricata	WCA8
broomrape, thistle	Orobanche reticulata	WCA8
butterfly-orchid, greater	Platanthera chlorantha	CITES2
butterfly-orchid, lesser	Platanthera bifolia	CITES2
cabbage, Lundy	Rhynchosinapis wrightii	WCA8
calamint, wood	Calamintha sylvatica	WCA8
catchfly, alpine	Lychnis alpina	WCA8
centaury, slender	Centaurium tenuiflorum	WCA8
cinquefoil, rock	Potentilla rupestris	WCA8
clary, meadow	Salvia pratensis	WCA8
club-rush, triangular	Scirpus triqueter	WCA8
clubmoss, alpine	Diphasiastrum alpinum	ECH5
clubmoss, fir	Huperzia selago	ECH5
clubmoss, interrupted	Lycopodium annotinum	ECH5
clubmoss, Issler's	Diphasiastrum complanatum	ECH5
clubmoss, marsh	Lycopodiella inundata	ECH5
clubmoss, stag's-horn	Lycopodium clavatum	ECH5
colt's-foot, purple	Homogyne alpina	WCA8
cotoneaster, wild	Cotoneaster integerrimus	WCA8
cottongrass, slender	Eriophorum gracile	WCA8
cow-wheat, field	Melampyrum arvense	WCA8
crocus, sand	Romulea columnae	WCA8

Common English name	Species	Protection (see key at start of Tables)
cudweed, broad-leaved	*Filago pyramidata*	WCA8
cudweed, Jersey	*Gnaphalium luteoalbum*	WCA8
cudweed, red-tipped	*Filago lutescens*	WCA8
cut-grass	*Leersia oryzoides*	WCA8
diapensia	*Diapensia lapponica*	WCA8
dock, shore	*Rumex rupestris*	BC1 ECH2,4 WCA8
eryngo, field	*Eryngium campestre*	WCA8
fern, Dickie's bladder	*Cystopteris dickieana*	WCA8
fern, Killarney	*Trichomanes speciosum*	BC1 ECH2,4 WCA8
fleabane, alpine	*Erigeron borealis*	WCA8
fleabane, small	*Pulicaria vulgaris*	WCA8
fleawort, South Stack	*Tephroseris integrifolia* ssp. *maritima*	WCA8
galingale, brown	*Cyperus fuscus*	WCA8
gentian, alpine	*Gentiana nivalis*	WCA8
gentian, dune	*Gentianella uliginosa*	WCA8
gentian, early	*Gentianella anglica*	BC1 ECH2,4 WCA8
gentian, fringed	*Gentianella ciliata*	WCA8
gentian, spring	*Gentiana verna*	WCA8
germander, cut-leaved	*Teucrium botrys*	WCA8
germander, water	*Teucrium scordium*	WCA8
gladiolus, wild	*Gladiolus illyricus*	WCA8
goosefoot, stinking	*Chenopodium vulvaria*	WCA8
grass-poly	*Lythrum hyssopifolia*	WCA8
ground-pine	*Ajuga chamaepitys*	WCA8
hare's-ear, sickle-leaved	*Bupleurum falcatum*	WCA8
hare's-ear, small	*Bupleurum baldense*	WCA8
hawk's-beard, stinking	*Crepis foetida*	WCA8
hawkweed, North Roe	*Hieracium northroense*	WCA8
hawkweed, Shetland	*Hieracium zetlandicum*	WCA8
hawkweed, weak-leaved	*Hieracium attenuatifolium*	WCA8
heath, blue	*Phyllodoce caerulea*	WCA8
helleborine, broad-leaved	*Epipactis helleborine*	CITES2
helleborine, dark-red	*Epipactis atrorubens*	CITES2

Common English name	Species	Protection (see key at start of Tables)
helleborine, green-flowered	Epipactis phyllanthes	CITES2
helleborine, narrow-leaved	Cephalanthera longifolia	CITES2
helleborine, marsh	Epipactis palustris	CITES2
helleborine, narrow-lipped	Epipactis leptochila	CITES2
helleborine, red	Cephalanthera rubra	CITES2 WCA8
helleborine, violet	Epipactis purpurata	CITES2
helleborine, white	Cephalanthera damasonium	CITES2
helleborine, Young's	Epipactis youngiana	CITES2 WCA8
horsetail, branched	Equisetum ramosissimum	WCA8
hound's-tongue, green	Cynoglossum germanicum	WCA8
knawel, perennial	Scleranthus perennis	WCA8
knotgrass, sea	Polygonum maritimum	WCA8
lady's-slipper	Cypripedium calceolus	BC1 CITES2 ECH2,4 WCA8
lady's-tresses, autumn	Spiranthes spiralis	CITES2
lady's-tresses, creeping	Goodyera repens	CITES2
lady's-tresses, Irish	Spiranthes romanzoffiana	CITES2
lady's-tresses, summer	Spiranthes aestivalis	BC1 CITES2 ECH2,4
Lapland marsh-orchid,	Dactylorhiza lapponica	CITES2 WCA8
late spider-orchid	Ophrys fuciflora	CITES2 WCA8
leek, round-headed	Allium sphaerocephalon	WCA8
lettuce, least	Lactuca saligna	WCA8
lily, Snowdon	Lloydia serotina	WCA8
marsh-mallow, rough	Althaea hirsuta	WCA8
marsh-orchid, early	Dactylorhiza incarnata	CITES2
marsh-orchid, narrow-leaved	Dactylorhiza traunsteineri	CITES2
marsh-orchid, northern	Dactylorhiza purpurella	CITES2
marsh-orchid, southern	Dactylorhiza praetermissa	CITES2
marsh-orchid, western	Dactylorhiza majalis	CITES2
marshwort, creeping	Apium repens	BC1 ECH2,4 WCA8
Martin's ramping-fumitory	Fumaria martinii	WCA8
milk-parsley, Cambridge	Selinum carvifolia	WCA8
mudwort, Welsh	Limosella australis	WCA8

Common English name	Species	Protection (see key at start of Tables)
naiad, holly-leaved	*Najas marina*	WCA8
naiad, slender	*Najas flexilis*	BC1 ECH2,4 WCA8
orache, stalked	*Halimione pedunculata*	WCA8
orchid, bee	*Ophrys apifera*	CITES2
orchid, bird's-nest	*Neottia nidus-avis*	CITES2
orchid, bog	*Hammarbya paludosa*	CITES2
orchid, burnt	*Orchis ustulata*	CITES2
orchid, coralroot	*Corallorrhiza trifida*	CITES2
orchid, dense-flowered	*Neotinea maculata*	CITES2
orchid, early-purple	*Orchis mascula*	CITES2
orchid, fen	*Liparis loeselii*	BC1 CITES2 ECH2,4 WCA8
orchid, fly	*Ophrys insectifera*	CITES2
orchid, fragrant	*Gymnadenia conopsea*	CITES2
orchid, frog	*Coeloglossum viride*	CITES2
orchid, ghost	*Epipogium aphyllum*	CITES2 WCA8
orchid, green-winged	*Orchis morio*	CITES2
orchid, lady	*Orchis purpurea*	CITES2
orchid, lizard	*Himantoglossum hircinum*	CITES2 WCA8
orchid, man	*Aceras anthropophorum*	CITES2
orchid, military	*Orchis militaris*	CITES2 WCA8
orchid, monkey	*Orchis simia*	CITES2 WCA8
orchid, musk	*Herminium monorchis*	CITES2
orchid, pyramidal	*Anacamptis pyramidalis*	CITES2
orchid, small-white	*Pseudorchis albida*	CITES2
pear, Plymouth	*Pyrus cordata*	WCA8
penny-cress, perfoliate	*Thlaspi perfoliatum*	WCA8
pennyroyal	*Mentha pulegium*	WCA8
pigmyweed	*Crassula aquatica*	WCA8
pink, Cheddar	*Dianthus gratianopolitanus*	WCA8
pink, childing	*Petrorhagia nanteuilii*	WCA8
pink, Deptford	*Dianthus armeria*	WCA8 (England & Wales only)
ragwort, fen	*Senecio paludosus*	WCA8
rampion, spike	*Phyteuma spicatum*	WCA8

VERSION 02.2/CBEB 0501

Common English name	Species	Protection (see key at start of Tables)
restharrow, small	Ononis reclinata	WCA8
rock-cress, alpine	Arabis alpina	WCA8
rock-cress, Bristol	Arabis stricta	WCA8
sandwort, Norwegian	Arenaria norvegica	WCA8
sandwort, Teesdale	Minuartia stricta	WCA8
saxifrage, drooping	Saxifraga cernua	WCA8
saxifrage, marsh	Saxifraga hirculus	BC1 ECH2,4 WCA8
saxifrage, tufted	Saxifraga cespitosa	WCA8
snowdrop[a]	Galanthus nivalis	CITES2 ECH5 (if native)
Solomon's-seal, whorled	Polygonatum verticillatum	WCA8
spearwort, adder's-tongue	Hanunculus ophioglossifolius	WCA8
speedwell, fingered	Veronica triphyllos	WCA8
speedwell, spiked	Veronica spicata	WCA8
spider-orchid, early	Ophrys sphegodes	CITES2 WCA8
spike-rush, dwarf	Eleocharis parvula	WCA8
spotted-orchid, common	Dactylorhiza fuchsii	CITES2
spotted-orchid, heath	Dactylorhiza maculata	CITES2
star-of-Bethlehem, early	Gagea bohemica	WCA8
starfruit	Damasonium alisma	WCA8
strapwort	Corrigiola litoralis	WCA8
twayblade	Listera ovata	CITES2
twayblade, lesser	Listera cordata	CITES2
violet, fen	Viola persicifolia	WCA8
viper's-grass	Scorzonera humilis	WCA8
water-plantain, floating	Luronium natans	BC1 ECH2,4 WCA8
water-plantain, ribbon-leaved	Alisma gramineum	WCA8
wood-sedge, starved	Carex depauperata	WCA8
woodsia, alpine	Woodsia alpina	WCA8
woodsia, oblong	Woodsia ilvensis	WCA8
wormwood, field	Artemisia campestris	WCA8

[a] Except seeds, pollen/polinia, seedlings/tissue cultures produced *in vitro*, cut flowers from artificially propagated plants.

Common English name	Species	Protection (see key at start of Tables)
woundwort, downy	*Stachys germanica*	WCA8
woundwort, limestone	*Stachys alpina*	WCA8
yellow-rattle, greater	*Rhinanthus serotinus*	WCA8

Lactuca saligna L.
least lettuce

APPENDIX: EUROPEAN PROTECTED SPECIES ESTABLISHED IN BRITAIN

TABLE 8: EUROPEAN PROTECTED SPECIES WHICH ARE ESTABLISHED IN THE WILD IN BRITAIN

The species listed here are protected by European legislation/convention and have become established in the wild in Great Britain. Britain is not, however, normally considered as part of their natural range and expert legal advice should be sought on precise status and implications. Under the Wildlife and Countryside Act (subject to various provisions) it is an offence to release these species or allow them to escape[a].

Scientific name	Common English name	Remarks
Alytes obstetricans	midwife toad	Established *e.g.* in Bedfordshire, Yorkshire.
Astacus astacus	noble crayfish	Escapes may be found in suitable water bodies. Limited protection under ECH only to possible need to control taking & exploitation.
Bombina variegata	yellow-bellied toad	Unmistakable if found.
Cervus spp	some deer and hybrids	See note below.
Elaphe longissima	Aesculapian snake	Young similar to *Natrix natrix*.
Emys orbicularis	European pond terrapin	Unlikely to be confused with any native reptile.
Hyla arborea	European tree frog	Colony recorded in New Forest (viability doubtful).
Podarcis muralis	common wall lizard	A few colonies on British mainland.
Rana ridibunda	marsh frog	Southern England (*e.g.* Romney marsh).
Rana esculenta	edible frog	Occasional in southern/eastern England.
Rhodeus sericeus	bitterling	Established in Cheshire, Lancashire, Cambridgeshire. ECH covers ssp. *amarus*.
Siluris glanis	wels, Danube catfish	Established in south-east central England.
Triturus alpestris	alpine newt	Shropshire, Berkshire, Sussex and elsewhere.
Triturus carnifex =*T. cristatus carnifex*	Italian crested newt	Very similar to *Triturus cristatus cristatus* but less warty.

Note on deer of the genus *Cervus* and hybrids of that genus. A variation of Schedule 9 of the Wildlife and Countryside Act came into force on 28 April 1999. This variation adds the following taxa to Part 1 of Schedule 9 of the Act (prohibition of release or allowing to escape into the wild):

Any hybrid of *Cervus nippon* (sika deer) in Britain;

With respect to the Outer Hebrides and the islands of Arran, Islay, Jura and Rum only, any species of *Cervus* (this includes red and sika deer) and any hybrid of the genus *Cervus*.

Sika and red deer have limited protection in Europe under BC3.

---

[a] There are various provisions in the Wildlife and Countryside Act to prohibit the introduction of exotic species of both animals and plants to the wild in Britain, not always effective as the above list indicates.